THE
HAZARD COMMUNICATION
ANSWER
BOOK

1st Edition

Mark McGuire Moran

1st Edition

ISBN 13: 978-1-890966-73-7

ISBN 10: 1890966-73--7

Printed in the United States of America
11-28-2011   5432

TABLE OF CONTENTS

PREFACE .... **xvi**
ABOUT THE AUTHOR.. **xvii**
INTRODUCTION .... **xxi**

PART ONE:

WHAT ARE THE NEW CHANGES TO THE HAZARD
COMMUNICATION STANDARD.. 1

CHAPTER ONE: WHAT IS GHS?................................... 3

GHS Meets HCS.. 6
Why was the GHS developed?................................... 8
How was the GHS Created?...................................... 11
When will the State Plans have to
Publish a Final Hazcom standard?............................ 14
Is there a Need to modify this Regulation?.................. 15
What Industries are affected by the
Revised Hazcom standard? 17
What are the Requirements to comply
With the new Hazcom standard?................................ 20
Transportation Pictograms 21
Physical & Environmental Hazard Symbols..................... 22
Allocation of label elements................................. 23
Transport and Emergency Responders.......................... 23
Federal Agencies Affected by Hazcom Revision............... 24
Environmental Protection Agency (EPA)
Occupational Safety Health Administration (OSHA)........... 25
The Department of Transportation (DOT) 25
The Consumer Product Safety Commission, (CPSC) 25
OSHA Standards Affected by the Hazcom revision........... 26
General Industry Standards 29 CFR 1910..................... 30
Construction Industry Standards 29 CFR 1926............... 31
Maritime Industry Standards 29 CFR 1915, 1917&1918....32

CHAPTER TWO:

HOW IS GHS TO BE APPLIED TO HAZCOM? 33
Are all Chemicals Covered by the GHS?...........................35
Will all Hazardous Chemicals require a GHS Label
and Safety Data Sheet?...36
What does a Label look like?..37
USA Examples.. 39
Agricultural Chemicals and Pesticides..........................41
International Example............................... 41
European Union Label..41
How will the GHS impact existing regulations?...................43
What is meant by GHS Building Blocks?...........................44
How the GHS Building Blocks should be applied?.............45
What does Classification mean?......................... 48
What are the GHS Physical Hazards?...............................49
A Comparison of The Old &
New Hazard Communication Standard 58
General Provisions Comparison 59
Scope Comparison 64
Application Comparison...72
Definitions Comparison..75
Hazard Determination/Classification Comparison..............87
Comparison of Label Elements..91
Workplace Labeling Comparison 97
Updating Labels Comparison..100
MSDS/SDS Comparison...102
Updating MSDS/SDS 109
Information & Training Comparison 111
Trade Secrets/CBI Comparison......................................114
Multiple Hazards/Precedence Comparison.....................124
Comparison of Health Hazards 134
Comparison of Physical Hazards 134
Label Examples 159

CHAPTER THREE:

WHAT ARE THE NEW CHANGES IN THE GHS/HAZARD
COMMUNICATION STANDARD?

WHAT ARE THE NEW CHANGES IN THE GHS/HAZARD COMMUNICATION STANDARD?..................... 163

Introduction... 165
New Criteria for Classification of
Chemicals 167
Treatment of Mixtures... 170
Changes in Hazard Classes and Criteria,
And Procedures for Classification 171
What are the New Changes in the Labels?..................... 172
What are Symbols/Pictograms under the New Hazcom
Standard?.. 173
What is required on Workplace labeling?......................... 177
Updating Labels... 179
Skull and Crossbones Pictogram 183
Exclamation Mark Pictogram 187
Corrosion Pictogram... 194
Environment Pictogram 199
Flame Pictogram 201
Flame over Circle Pictogram 206
Exploding Bomb Pictogram 213
Gas Cylinder Pictogram..223
Health Hazard Pictogram 227
What are the New Changes in Material?
Safety Data Sheets (MSDS)?...245
SDS Preparation..246
SDS Format..247
SDS Sheets 252
What are the New Changes in
Employee Information and Training?..............................256
The GHS/OSHA regulation mandates
3 New Changes in Training 257

PART TWO: HOW IS THE HAZARD COMMUNICATION STANDARD ENFORCED?..260

CHAPTER FOUR: HOW WILL THE HAZARD COMMUNICATION/GHS STANDARD BE ENFORCED?...261

How are Inspection Targets Chosen?...............................264
How to Avoid OSHA Hazard Communication Fines? 265
The Hazard Communication Standard
Can be broken into 4 parts..266
Written Plan 266
Labels 266
Safety Data Sheets..267
Training 267
Hazard Communication Program Explained 268
How will the OSHA Inspector examine
our Written Hazard Communication Program? 269
Labels and Other Forms of Warning Explained...............273
How will the OSHA Inspector examine our Labels?..........276
Safety Data Sheets Explained 277
Factors that determine if Safety Data Sheets are readily accessible? 280
How will the OSHA Inspector Examine
our Safety Data Sheet? 283
Employee Information &Training Explained 286
How will the OSHA Inspector examine
our Training program? 289
Hazard Communication Compliance Checklist.................292

CHAPTER FIVE: QUESTIONS & ANSWERS
ON THE NEW HAZCOM/GHS STANDARD...................... 303

What does GHS mean in the newly revised Hazard
Communication standard?... 304

 Does OSHA send you updated Safety Data
Sheets (SDSs) for the products your company uses?...... 305

What hazardous chemicals need to be communicated to
employees upon their hire? Can I give them a copy of all of our
hazardous chemicals (by name) in a single document, or do I
only give them the name of chemicals they may be handling in
their specific department? Furthermore, what is a
"hazardous chemical"? What rating dictates that a chemical
must be on this list?.. 305

Does a company have to provide Safety Data Sheets
(SDS's) to a customer? 308

What is the Purpose of the Hazard
Communication Standard? 309

When will the revised Hazard Communication/
GHS standard go into effect? 310

What are the new changes to the Hazard Communication
/GHS standard that our company needs to know?........... 311

Are there other regulatory agencies involved in this
final rule besides OSHA that we should be
concerned with? 312

Is the HAZCOM Standard applicable
to an office Environment?... 313

Is a Safety Data Sheet (SDS) required
for NoN-Hazardous Chemicals? 313

Are pharmaceutical drugs in a retail establishment which is
packaged for sale to consumers exempt from the Hazard
Communication standard (HCS)?. 314

If the manufacturer cannot provide a SDS for a covered
drug, must the pharmacy document attempt to obtain a SDS?
....314

What are the requirements to obtain Safety Data Sheets
from manufacturers of drugs and other products which
are not received by a hospital in final form? 315

I work at a small business where we use chemical products
such as thinners, adhesives, and paints. Could you please
clarify whether or not the use of consumer art products by
employees would meet the consumer products exemption
under the Hazard Communication standard? 316

My office purchases products such as Windex and Office
cleaner so that their employees may clean their work stations.
Would the office cleaning products used by my employees
come under the consumer products exemption of the HCS
and not require a Safety Data Sheet or Training? 317

The Hazard Communication Standard (HCS) as it pertains to
the electronic transmittal of Safety Data Sheets (SDSs). Is it
acceptable under OSHA compliance to have the electronic
transmission, storage, and dissemination of
SDSs?..318

Is there an acceptable alternative to having drivers maintain
an in-vehicle library of Safety Data Sheets to cover every
commercial sale which may be made during the day? 320

What are the definitions of Pictograms/Precautionary statements and Unclassified Hazards mean? 321

Are there any changes in the Hazard Communication standard that will affect other OSHA standards? 322

What are the State Plan States plans doing after the Hazard Communication regulation is final? 323

Our company produces gaskets and it is considered an "article" under the Hazard Communication Standard (HCS). Articles do not present a hazardous exposure to employees and are exempt from coverage under the standard. Can you tell me whether our product is an "article" or a "hazardous chemical."? 323

Can a Written program like the Hazard Communication program be kept solely in an Electronic Format? 325

What are the interpretations of the Written Hazard Communication Program (HCP) requirements of employers on Multi- Employer Worksites? 326

What are the relationships between the Hazard Communication Standard (HCS), 29 CFR 1910.1200, and Access to Employee Medical Records, 29 CFR 1910.1020, as they relate to maintenance of Safety Data Sheets (SDS) and the Written Hazard Communication Program? 328

What are "Pictograms"? 329

What does Hazard Statements/Precautionary Statements mean under the Hazard Communication Standard? 332

Would a European Union GHS label be sufficient to meet OSHA's current Hazard Communication Standard ?........334

What are the Container Labeling Requirements under HAZCOM?. 335

How do I know if my Safety Data Sheets (SDS) are in compliance with the New Hazcom standard? 336

Do I have to keep every Safety Data Sheet that our companies receive?...337

Does OSHA Really Require Employers to Keep SDSs for 30 Years?..337

If I have the same Chemical from a different manufacturer, Do I need to keep their entire Safety Data Sheet? 339

Can I throw away outdated Safety Data Sheets? 339

I have encountered in providing Safety Data Sheets is that you "use distributors and we do not know when a first shipment to a customer has occurred." OSHA recognizes this difficulty, and has never required manufacturers to automatically provide copies of SDSs to the end use customer. As the manufacturer may have no way of knowing who these customers are. The requirements of the Hazard Communication standard are based upon a downstream flow of information from chemical manufacturers to distributors and/or employers and ultimately, to affected employees are this the way it works?..............340

What if I need a Safety Data Sheet and the Manufacturer of the business no longer exists?..341

How come I don't always get Safety Data Sheets when I order chemicals? I thought manufacturers of chemicals were required to give me one for every chemical I purchase? ..341

When does a Safety Data Sheet need to be revised or
replaced?..343

Do I have to use Hard Copies or can I use a Computer
Database to maintain Safety Data Sheets?......................344

What does the term "ready access" requirement
and what is a "barrier" to ready access mean? 345

What are the Penalties for NoN-Compliance
with Safety Data Sheets? 345

We have a large worksite. Does having one site-wide
SDS repository to maintain our Safety Data Sheets
Satisfy OSHA Requirements 346

What OSHA requirements are there for Contractors
who work on Multi-Employer Worksites?..........................346

Must the Pharmacy keep Safety Data Sheets (SDS's)
for products that do not contain hazardous chemicals
and are intended to be crushed or mixed prior to use? 347

How does OSHA expect me to organize my
Safety Data Sheets or System? 348

Some of my Employees don't speak English. Do I
Have to make any special provisions for these workers?. 348

Would OSHA take enforcement action under the current
regulations against employers or users of a product that
has been appropriately labeled according to European
Union GHS requirements? 350

Under what conditions can employers rely on Safety
Data Sheets services to make available a specific
chemical used by that employer? 350

What happens after the retailer's regular business
hours or when the manufacturer's facility is closed
on the weekend? 351

It seems that trying to maintain Safety Data Sheets
at the retail level is a waste of time could you please
explain this to me? 352

If Safety Data Sheets (SDS(s) are made available via computer
terminal and employees are properly trained to access them, is
a printer necessary or can the SDS simply be read on the
screen? 353

If an Employer has employees who do not understand verbal
English (re: receive work task instructions in a language other
than English), must that employer provide the training
information in a language that is Comprehensive? 354

Is it OSHA policy to require employers to obtain Safety Data
Sheets to ordinary consumer products used by its employees,
and to Train the employees in the safe use of these products?
While the training is invaluable, there is effort involved in
obtaining the needed SDS and conducting the Training?.355

Can a contractor's association train union employees
under the Hazard communication standard," or "should
 each contractor train each employee irrespective of the
associations." Is each employer responsible for training
under the Hazard Communication Standard?...................356

Does OSHA expect that every worker will be trained and able to recite all of the information on the Safety Data Sheets in the Workplace? 358

In the Construction industry, the scope of the Hazcom standard is to include all employers with employees exposed to hazardous substances, what is the training requirement when we receive information on the potential hazards from occupational exposures to hazardous substances that may be exposed from other workplaces? 359

Is it acceptable to distribute copies of Safety Data Sheets (SDS's) and consider that to be training? 361

What is the requirement for additional Employee training whenever new hazards are identified? 362

Who is responsible for Hazard Communication training of the temporary employee? The Temporary Agency or the Employer? 363

The Hazard Communication Standard requires training on hazardous chemicals in the work area at the time of the initial assignment and whenever a new hazard was is introduced into the work place. When does the initial assignment begin and who is responsible for the Initial Training and the on-going Training? 364

APPENDICIES 365

A. Sample Written Hazard Communication Plan..........366
B. Sample Letter Requesting a Safety Data Sheet.......399
C. Acknowledgement of Receipt of Hazard
   Communication Training Form...................402
D. Sample of a Complete Safety Data Sheet.................404
E. Sample Contractor Notification Letter......................411
F. Sample Safety Data Sheet Policy 414

GLOSSARY................421

INDEX................445

I Welcome Your Questions!

In order to keep the success of this book going, I welcome your questions for changes to future editions. Please feel free to email me. **mmoran@oshamadeasy.com**

PREFACE

This book is an effort to place everything that Employers and Employees need to know about the revised **Hazard Communication Standard/GHS.** It is a reference book, designed to be consulted frequently! Information that every employer should have is contained within the pages of this book.

ABOUT THE AUTHOR

About Simplifi Safety, Inc.

Mark McGuire Moran is the President of Simplifi Safety, a management consulting firm that specializes in occupational safety and health. The firm is engaged in keeping its clients abreast of administrative and legislative developments in occupational safety and health laws, analyzing their effect upon business and industry. The firm's clients include employers throughout the country engaged in all aspects of business.

In 1970, my father, Robert D. Moran, Esq. was appointed by President Richard M. Nixon as the first Chairman of the U.S. Occupational Safety and Health Review Commission (OSHA). He was often referred to as the **"Grandfather of OSHA" by President Nixon;** he served in this position for over seven years. My father was responsible for heading a government task force that planned the implementation of the OSHA Act and the eventual creation of OSHA.

Mr. Moran is certified by the U.S. Department of Labor as an accredited instructor in compliance with OSHA requirements. Mr. Moran also worked on Capitol Hill as a legislative assistant to Bill McCollum (R-Fl). He wrote the entire scripts for the American Subcontractors Association on OSHA's Fall Protection Standard, and Ergonomics. Mr. Moran also represents various national trade Associations.

Mr. Moran is also a speaker who makes presentations at conferences sponsored by many trade associations, including the National Safety Council.

Whether you have one employee or hundreds...as their employer, you are responsible for their safety. It's not enough to think you're in compliance. It's a situation all too common: you assume you're in compliance with OSHA, but during a routine inspection, you are shocked at the number of violations you've racked up (and the hefty fines your company will have to pay).

With over 25 years experience helping businesses like yours comply with OSHA regulations, I look forward to serving you, and welcome any questions/comments you might have.

Contact me to learn how I can help you reduce accidents, meet federal, state and local legal requirements, reduce costs, and most importantly, protect your greatest assets - your employees.

Mark McGuire Moran
President. Simplifi Safety, Inc.

Visit **www.oshamadeasy.com.**

DEDICATION

The author wishes to give special acknowledgement to my late father, **Robert D. Moran Esq.** He was the 1st chairman of the Occupational Safety and Health Review Commission (OSHRC), who I worked for and he was not only my father, but was my mentor and inspiration in life.

I learned as much as I could from him as his knowledge of OSHA was endless. His considerable wit, charm, inspired me to be where I am today. Thanks Dad you did a great job!

Introduction

Hazard Communication

The OSHA Hazard Communication Standard, also known as HazCom, HCS, 29 CFR 1910.1200, and Right to Know among others, is a U.S. regulation that governs the evaluation and communication of hazards associated with chemicals in the workplace.

OSHA is aligning HCS with the Globally Harmonized System (GHS), a global hazard communication system developed by the United Nations (UN) that standardizes the classification of chemicals and the communication of hazards via labels and MSDSs. With GHS alignment, the classification of chemicals will include the categorization of hazards based upon severity. Other changes will significantly alter labels and safety data sheets.

Labels will now have Six Standardized Elements: **1). Product Identifier, 2). Manufacturer Information, 3). Signal Word, 4). Pictograms, 5) Hazard Statements; and 6).Precautionary Statements.** Also under GHS, safety data sheets are referred to as SDSs, dropping the M from MSDSs. More importantly, these SDSs have 16 sections which are arranged in a strict ordering. Because of these and other changes, employers should expect to update their entire safety data sheets.

The Hazard Communication Answer Book will help you understand all the new changes to the standard. The HCS is characterized as a performance-oriented standard. This means that your company has the flexibility to comply with the standard in a way that best fits your business practices and meets the performance requirements of the standard.

The most significant change to the revised Hazard Communication Standard is the **Pictograms.** A Pictogram means a graphical composition that may include a symbol plus other elements, such as a border, background pattern or color that conveys specific information. All hazard pictograms should be in the shape of a square set on a point (diamond). There are a total of **Nine (9) Pictograms** explained in the book.

This Book also includes a **Written Hazard Communication Program** companies can customize on a CD. This will help you be in compliance with the New Standard!

How to use this Book:

Every employer should read Part One. This will provide the reader with an incentive to read Part Two as well.

This Book is divided into 2 Parts:

Part 1: This explains what the new changes are to the Hazard Communication/GHS standard. It explains how to be in compliance!

Part 2: How the Hazard Communication Standard is enforced and how employers can cope with OSHA enforcement!

PART 1:

WHAT ARE THE NEW CHANGES TO THE HAZARD COMMUNICATION STANDARD?

- Chapter 1-

What is GHS?

Chapter Highlights:

- Why was the GHS developed?
- What Industries are affected by the Hazcom standard?
- What are the new Requirements to comply with the Hazcom standard?
- What Federal Agencies are affected by the Hazcom revision?

The GHS is an acronym for "The Globally Harmonized System of Classification and Labeling of Chemicals". It is a comprehensive approach to:

- Defining health, physical and environmental hazards of chemicals;

- Creating classification processes that use available data on chemicals for comparison with the defined hazard criteria; and

- Communicating hazard information, as well as protective measures, on labels and Safety Data Sheets (SDS).

The *Globally Harmonized System of Classification and Labeling of Chemicals* (GHS) is not a regulation or standard, but a system for classifying and labeling chemicals. This system was developed in order to harmonize chemical labeling and classification internationally.

At the present time, many different hazard communication systems are in use worldwide. While the existing hazard communication laws and regulations are similar in general—for example, many countries require that a hazardous chemical be accompanied by a safety data sheet (SDS)—there are numerous differences in hazard definitions and label and SDS requirements. As a result, some chemicals are classified differently in different jurisdictions, and manufacturers have to produce multiple versions of their labels and SDSs for international trade.

Recognizing the complex nature of the present system for managing hazardous chemicals, the 1992 United Nations Conference on Environment and Development established an international mandate to create a globally harmonized system for classification and labeling. Over the ensuing years, the GHS was developed on a consensus basis with support from major stakeholders such as national governments, industry, and workers. This effort was coordinated by a group working under the Inter-organizational Program for the Sound Management of Chemicals (IOMC).

The GHS was formally adopted by the United Nations Committee of Experts on the Transport of Dangerous Goods and the Globally Harmonized System of Classification and Labelling of Chemicals in December 2002, and was endorsed by the United Nations Economic and Social Council in July 2003. The GHS is not binding; rather, it represents a set of "building blocks" that each nation can elect to implement within its own regulatory framework.

The Globally Harmonized System is an international system proposed by experts under the guidance of the United Nations Subcommittee for GHS. It establishes new rules for hazardous chemicals in transportation, workplace use and consumer use, as well as special rules for pesticides. GHS also includes new Safety Data Sheet (SDS's) requirements and new hazard symbols. It comprises standards for:

- **Classifying chemicals**
- **Symbols for hazards**
- **Labeling requirement**
- **Safety Data Sheet requirements**

[T]he GHS offers a standardized and specific approach to the creation of labels and Safety Data Sheets (SDS), with a set format, content and order. The GHS has an established set of hazard criteria and employs the use of standardized pictograms. We believe these elements of the GHS, when incorporated into the HCS, will assist in generating labels and SDS's that are vastly more consistent and comprehensible in comparison to the current MSDS's and labels. The improved consistency will also increase the ability to communicate the hazard information to workers. OSHA is also changing the name of the "material safety data sheets" for the substance specific standards to "safety data sheets."

GHS Meets HCS

OSHA is modifying the Hazard Communication Standard (HAZCOM) with the Globally Harmonized System of Classification and Labeling of Chemicals (GHS). Over 40 million workers in more than 5 million workplaces are expected to be impacted.

The HAZCOM currently:

- Requires chemical manufacturers and importers to label containers and prepare MSDS's Sheets;
- Requires employers to have a HAZCOM written program for workers who have exposures or potential exposures; and
- Train employees.

GHS will:

- Adopts a standardized method of hazard classification leading to an increase in quality and consistency of information provided to employees and employers;
- Classifies chemicals by their health and physical hazards; and
- Specifies hazard communication specifics for labeling and SDS's.

Major changes to HAZCOM:

- Specific criteria for classification of health and physical hazards of chemicals and mixtures.
- Manufacturers and importers must use standardized labeling methods that include signal word, pictograms, and hazard statements.
- MSDS's will have a specific 16-section format; and
- Workers must be trained within 3 years of the final rule on the recognition and understanding of the GHS labeling and SDS system.

Why was the GHS developed?

The production and use of chemicals is fundamental to all economies. The global chemical business is more than a $1.7 trillion per year.

In the U.S., chemicals are more than a $450 billion business and exports are greater than $80 billion per year. Chemicals directly or indirectly affect our lives and are essential to our food, our health, and our lifestyle. The widespread use of chemicals has resulted in the development of sector-specific regulations (transport, production, workplace, and agriculture, trade, and consumer products). Having readily available information on the hazardous properties of chemicals, and recommended control measures, allows the production, transport, use and disposal of chemicals to be managed safely. Thus, human health and the environment are protected.

The sound management of chemicals should include systems through which chemical hazards are identified and communicated to all who are potentially exposed. These groups include workers, consumers, emergency responders and the public. It is important to know what chemicals are present and used their hazards to human health and the environment, and the means to control them. A number of classification and labeling systems, each addressing specific use patterns and groups of chemicals, exist at the national, regional and international levels. The existing hazard classification and labeling systems address potential exposure to chemicals in all the types of use settings listed above. While the existing laws and regulations are similar, they are different enough to require multiple labels for the same product both within the U.S. and in international trade and to require multiple safety data sheets for the same product in international trade. Several U.S. regulatory agencies and various countries have different requirements for hazard definitions as well as for information to be included on labels or material safety data sheets

Figure 1.1

Acute oral toxicity LD$_{50}$ (mg/kg)						
Organization/Country/ Regulation or Standard	High 0		Hazard < 50	< 500	Low < 5000	
ANSI/US/A 129.1	< 50 Highly Toxic		> 50 < 500 Toxic	> 500 < 2000 Harmful		
OSHA/US/HCS	< 50 Highly Toxic		> 50 < 500 Toxic			
EPA/US/FIFRA	0 ≤ 50 Toxicity Category I		> 50 ≤ 500 Toxicity Category II	> 500 < 5000 Toxic Category III	> 5000 Toxicity Category IV	
CPSC/US/FHSA	< 50 Highly Toxic		> 50 ≤ 500 Toxic			
GHS	≤ 5	> 5 ≤ 50	> 50 ≤ 300	> 300 ≤ 2000	> 2000 ≤ 5000	
DOT/US	< 5 Picking Group 1	> 5 < 50 Picking Group II	> 50 < 200 (solid) > 50 > 500 (liquid) Picking Group III			
NFPA/US	≤ 5 Hazard Category	> 5 ≤ 50 Hazard Categor	> 50 ≤ 500 Hazard Category	> 500 ≤ 2000 Hazard	> 2000 Hazard Categor	

	4	y 3	2	Category 1	y 0	
NPCA/US/HMIS	≤ 1 Toxicity Rating 4	> 1 ≤ 50 Toxicity Rating 3	> 50 ≤ 500 Toxicity Rating 2	> 500 ≤ 5000 Toxicity Rating 1	> 5000 Toxicity Rating 0	
EU	< 25 Very Toxic	> 25 > 200 Toxic		> 200 < 2000 Harmful		
WHMIS/Canada	≤ 50 Very Toxic WHMIS Class D, Division 1, Subdivision A		> 50 ≤ 500 Toxic WHMIS Class D, Division 1, Subdivision B			
Australia/NOHSC	< 25 Very Toxic	> 25 < 200 Toxic		> 200 < 2000 Harmful		
Mexico	<1 Extremely Toxic	>20 < 50 Highly Toxic	> 50 < 500 Moderately Toxic	> 500 < 5000 Mildly Toxic		
Malaysia	< 25 Very Toxic		200 to 500 Harmful			
Japan	< 30 Poisonous			300 to 3000 Powerful		
Korea	< 25 Very Toxic	> 50 < 200 Toxic		> 200 < 2000 Harmful		

The numerical values on the hazard index scale in the table are not to scale. For example, a product may be considered flammable or toxic by one agency or country, but not by another. We can see by comparing a few hazards how complex it is to comply with all domestic and global regulations.

Acute oral toxicity (LD_{50}) is a good example (Figure 1.1). Although most existing systems cover acute toxicity, we can see in the figure that what is considered hazardous varies considerably. These differences allow the same product to be hazardous in one country/system and not in another. At the very least, the same product has different labels and SDSs.

How was the GHS Created?

Many countries already have regulatory systems in place

for these types of requirements. These systems may be similar in content and approach, but their differences are significant enough to require multiple classifications, labels and safety data sheets for the same product when marketed in different countries or even in the same country when parts of the life cycle are covered by different regulatory authorities.

This leads to inconsistent protection for those potentially exposed to the chemicals, as well as creating extensive regulatory burdens on companies producing chemicals. For example, in the United States (U.S.) there are requirements for classification and labeling of chemicals for the Consumer Product Safety Commission (CPSC), the Department of Transportation (DOT), the Environmental Protection Agency (EPA), and the Occupational Safety and Health Administration (OSHA).

The GHS establishes agreed hazard classification and communication provisions with explanatory information on how to apply the system. The elements in the GHS supply a mechanism to meet the basic requirement of any hazard communication system, which is to decide if the chemical product produced and/or supplied is hazardous and to prepare a label and/or Safety Data Sheet as appropriate.

Regulatory authorities in countries adopting the GHS will thus take the agreed criteria and provisions, and implement them through their own regulatory process and procedures rather than simply incorporating the text of the GHS into their national requirements.

GHS provides countries with the regulatory building blocks to develop or modify existing national programs that address classification of hazards and transmittal of information about those hazards and associated protective measures. This helps to ensure the safe use of chemicals as they move through the product life cycle from "cradle to grave."

Chemical exposures result in a substantial number of serious injuries and illnesses among exposed employees. The Bureau of Labor Statistics estimates that employees suffered 55,400 illnesses that could be attributed to chemical exposures in 2007, the latest year for which data are available (BLS, 2008). In that same year, 17,340 chemical-source injuries and illnesses involved days away from work.

The HCS currently serves to ensure that information concerning chemical hazards and associated protective measures is provided to employers and employees. However, OSHA's experience, along with information acquired since the HCS was issued, indicates that modifications to the standard may be appropriate. OSHA believes that the changes, will substantially improve the quality and consistency of the information provided to employers and employees. The revisions to the HCS will enhance workplace protections, because better information will enable employers and employees to take measures that would result in a reduction in the number and severity of chemical-related injuries and illnesses.

> **OSHA estimates that 880,000 hazardous chemicals are currently used in the U.S. and over 40 million employees are now potentially exposed to hazardous chemicals in over 5 million workplaces.**

When will the State Plans have to publish a final Hazcom standard?

OSHA has 26 states and territories with their own OSHA-approved occupational safety and health plans.

These states must adopt comparable provisions of the Hazcom standard within six months after Federal OSHA publishes a final standard on GHS/Hazcom.

These States and territories are: Alaska, Arizona, California, Hawaii, Indiana, Iowa, Kentucky, Maryland, Michigan, Minnesota, Nevada, New Mexico, North Carolina, Oregon, Puerto Rico, South Carolina, Tennessee, Utah, Vermont, Virginia, Virgin Islands, Washington, and Wyoming. Connecticut, New Jersey and New York have OSHA approved State Plans that apply to State and local government employees only. Each state plan State's existing requirements will continue to be in effect until it adopts the required revisions.

Is there a Need to modify this Regulation?

Employees in work environments covered by the HCS are exposed to a variety of significant hazards that can and do cause serious injury and death. The HCS serves to assure that both employers and employees are provided needed information about chemical hazards that was not provided by markets in the absence of such a standard.

The HCS also facilitates interstate commerce by promoting consistency among Federal and individual State requirements. The changes would create uniformity standard for the presentation of risk information and, as such, would serve to improve the efficiency and effectiveness of the existing hazard communication system in the U.S., and to reduce unnecessary barriers to trade.

Hazard communication is currently addressed by many different international, national, and State authorities. These existing requirements are not always consistent and often contain different definitions of hazards and varying provisions for what information is required on labels and safety data sheets. Complying with these different rules results in increased costs for employers with hazardous chemicals in their workplace and for chemical manufacturers, distributors, and transporters involved in international trade. In addition to the effects on businesses, the different existing requirements result in workplaces receiving chemicals with varying information, with potential adverse impacts on the safety and health of employees.

The revisions to the OSHA HCS will standardize the hazard communication requirements for products used in U.S. workplaces, and thus provide employees with uniform and consistent hazard communication information. Secondarily, because these revisions would harmonize the U.S. system with international norms, they would facilitate international trade. The standard contains a number of changes to improve the performance of the U.S. hazard communication system:

> • Revised criteria for more consistent classification of chemical hazards;
>
> •Standardized signal words, pictograms, hazard statements, and precautionary statements on labels; and
>
> • A standardized format for SDSs. In short, GHS is a "uniformity standard" for the presentation of hazard information). In the case of GHS, manufacturers would be able to produce SDSs at lower cost, and users of SDSs would be able to more fully and quickly utilize the information contained in the SDSs, thereby reducing costs and, more importantly, better protect workers against chemical hazards.

What Industries are affected by the revised Hazcom standard?

The HCS covers a broad range of industries including

 General Industry (1910), Construction (1926) and Maritime (1915).

The standard is performance-oriented. OSHA believes that the detailed and specific classification requirements of the GHS would result in better, more consistent information being provided to employers and employees. Classification under the revised criteria would not only indicate the type of hazard, but would generally give an indication of the degree of severity of the hazard as well.

The HCS establishes requirements for minimum information that must be included on labels and SDSs, but does not provide specific language to convey the information or a format in which to provide it. The record indicated that a performance-oriented approach would reduce the need for chemical manufacturers and importers to revise these existing documents to comply with the HCS, thus reducing the cost impact of the standard. In recognition of the work that had been voluntarily completed, OSHA decided to allow labels and SDSs to be presented in any format desired, as long as the minimum information requirements of the standard were met.

The GHS is an internationally harmonized system for classifying chemical hazards and developing labels and safety data sheets. The GHS establishes a standardized16-section format for SDSs to provide a consistent sequence for presentation of information to SDS users. Items of primary interest to exposed employees and emergency responders are presented at the beginning of the document, while more technical information is presented later. Headings for the sections (For example, First Aid Measures, Handling and Storage) are standardized to facilitate locating information of interest. The harmonized data sheets are consistent with the order of information included in the voluntary industry consensus standard for safety data sheets.

The detailed criteria for classification are also expected to result in greater accuracy in hazard classification and more consistency among classifiers. By following the detailed criteria, classifiers are less likely to reach different interpretations of the same data. OSHA believes that standardized presentation of information on labels and safety data sheets would improve the comprehensibility of chemical hazard information. Employers and employees would be given the same core information on a chemical regardless of the supplier. Use of standardized pictograms would complement and reinforce the information provided through signal words and hazard statements. Pictograms are also anticipated to improve communication for those who are not functionally literate, or who are not literate in the language used on the label. The standardized format for SDSs is expected to make the information easier for users to find, with the information employees and emergency responders need most appearing in the beginning of the document for easy identification and reference. Standardized requirements for labels and SDSs are also expected to increase the accuracy of chemical hazard information.

With consistent presentation of information, the task of reviewing SDSs and labels to assure accuracy would be simplified. Individuals preparing and reviewing these documents should find it easier to identify any missing elements, and OSHA enforcement personnel should be able to more efficiently examine SDSs and labels when conducting inspections.

Compliance requirements for chemical users would be limited. Workplaces where chemicals are used would need to integrate the new approach into their hazard communication program, assuring that employees understand the pictograms and other information provided on labels and SDSs. Employers who use chemicals, and exposed employees, would benefit from receiving labels and safety data sheets presented in a consistent format. The information should be easier to find and comprehend, allowing it to be used more effectively for the protection of employees. Changing the HCS to make it conform to the GHS will also make it necessary to modify a number of other OSHA standards.

"It is expected that all of the GHS elements including labels that have the harmonized core information under the GHS, and safety data sheets will be supplemented by employee training to help ensure effective communication."

What are the New Requirements to comply with the Hazcom standard?

The three information components in this system labels, SDSs, and employee training are all essential to the effective functioning of the program. Labels provide a brief, conspicuous summary of hazard information at the site where the chemical is used. SDSs provide detailed technical information and serve as a reference source for exposed employees, industrial hygienists, safety professionals, emergency responders, health care professionals, and other interested parties. Training is designed to ensure that employees understand the chemical hazards in their workplace and are aware of protective measures to follow. Labels, SDSs, and training are complementary parts of a comprehensive hazard communication program each element reinforces the knowledge necessary for effective protection of employees.

The revisions would harmonize the U.S. system with international norms and therefore would facilitate international trade. The modifications to the Standard's collection of information requirements include: **(1)** Revised criteria for classification of chemical hazards; **(2)** revised labeling provisions that include requirements for use of standardized signal words, pictograms, hazard statements, and precautionary statements; **(3)** a specified format for safety data sheets; and **(4)** related revisions to definitions of terms used in the Standard and to requirements for employee training on labels and safety data sheets.

Transportation Pictograms

For transport, the pictograms prescribed by the UN Model Regulations on the Transport of Dangerous Goods should be used. Transport pictograms must have minimum dimensions of 100mm by 100mm, with exceptions for smaller pictograms on very small packaging and gas cylinders. Transport pictograms have symbol on upper half of label. The pictograms should be affixed to a background of contrasting color. See below.

Physical & Environmental Hazard Symbols

Hazard	Transport Symbols
Explosive	
Flammability: Liquid, Solid, Gas, Pyrophoric, Emit Flammable Gas	
Oxidizer Orga ic peroxide	
Gasses under Pressure	
Corrosive to Metals	

Allocation of Label elements

On packages covered by the UN Model Regulations on the Transport of Dangerous Goods: where a transport pictogram appears, a GHS pictogram for the same hazard should not appear. GHS pictograms not required for transport should not be displayed on freight containers, road vehicles or railway cars.

Pictograms will have a black symbol on white background with a red frame sufficiently wide enough to be clearly  visible. GHS gives the option of using a black border for packages that will not be exported. OSHA will require a red framed border, whether the package is for domestic or international use.

Transport and Emergency Responders

For hazardous products being transported, outer containers have required label elements, product identifier and hazard symbols. Transportation requirements are in addition to workplace or end use label requirements.

What Federal Agencies are Affected by the Hazcom revision?

In the U.S. there are four regulatory agencies that exercise jurisdiction over the revised Hazard Communication standard. They are:

1). Environmental Protection Agency (EPA) - Regulates pesticides and has other labeling authority under the Toxic Substances Control Act. (TSCA). The EPA has initiated a GHS review and is planning to issue new regulations to revise labels for pesticide products. It is likely that chemical companies' manufacturing pesticides would have to prepare new labels and, in the process, they will have to classify their products.

 Given the size and scale of the pesticide market in the United States and the importance of label review in the U.S. system of pesticide regulation, EPA recognizes that significant time and effort would be required to implement the GHS label changes and conduct effective outreach and education activities. After labeling rules and policies change, there would need to be time for a transition to the new labels. Implementation will also require coordination at a national and international level to avoid unnecessary disruptions.

2).Occupational Safety Health Administration (OSHA) Regulates chemicals in the workplace. It  requires chemical manufacturers, importers and employers to label containers and prepare SDS's Sheets; requires employers to have a HAZCOM written program for workers who have exposures or potential exposures; and train employees.

3). The Department of Transportation (DOT) – Regulates chemicals in transport and has adopted several elements of the GHS. These elements include the aspects of the GHS that directly affect the transport sector such as changes to the hazard classification criteria for toxic materials and flammable liquids.  Changes to regulations concerning environmentally hazardous substances will be made under a separate rulemaking, as the relevant criteria adopted by the GHS Sub-Committee will need to be considered by the EPA.

4). The Consumer Product Safety Commission, (CPSC), Regulates consumer products. The Consumer Product Safety Commission (CPSC) has begun a GHS review and expects to develop new regulations affecting consumer products containing chemical substances.  Consumer products such as soap, skin care products, perfumes, furniture polishes, detergent etc. will have to be classified for their health hazards and these agencies are not domestically harmonized in terms of definitions of hazards and other requirements. Many of these products are regulated under OSHA regulations if they are used in the workplace as non consumer products. When all four agencies adopt the GHS, the U.S. would have the additional benefit of harmonizing the overall U.S. approach to classification and labeling. Since most chemicals are produced in a workplace and shipped elsewhere, nearly every employer deals with at least two sets of Federal requirements. Thus every producer would be likely to experience some benefits from domestic harmonization.

OSHA Standards Affected by the Hazcom Revision

Substance Specific Health Standards

OSHA has reviewed all its standards and is modifying

standards in General Industry (29 CFR part 1910),Construction (29 CFR part 1926), and Shipyards,

Marine Terminals and Longshoring (29 CFR parts 1915, 1917 and 1918) that contain hazard classification and communication provisions in order that they will be internally consistent and aligned with the GHS modifications to the HCS. OSHA proposes to update substance specific health standards where they reference HCS or contain their own hazard communication requirements. OSHA is modifying these standards in the following areas:

• Revise the provisions covering workplace signs to require warning statements that are consistent with the GHS modifications to HCS;

• Revise all standards to reference the modified HCS for labels, safety data sheets, and training, and identify the hazards that need to be addressed;

• Maintain the requirement to avoid creating dust currently in some substance-specific health standards, but for which GHS modifications contain no equivalent statements at this time;

• Update most definitions in Occupational Exposure to Hazardous Chemicals in Laboratories, to maintain compatibility with the modified HCS; and

• Change the name Material Safety Data Sheets to Safety Data Sheets and require information on them to be compliant with GHS in content, format and order.

Most OSHA substance-specific health standards require hazard warning signs, usually for regulated areas, and the language required on the signs varies.

With the GHS revision, these standards retain the requirements for specific warning language for specific signs; however, OSHA is also to modifying the language to be compatible with GHS and consistent throughout the OSHA standards. The GHS classification process for a specific substance as proposed in this revision of the HCS will dictate the hazard warnings and the precautionary statements that will be required on the new GHS-compliant labels. OSHA believes that having signs and labels in the same formats and containing identical warnings for the same health effects will make it far easier for employers and employees to quickly recognize the hazard and the degree of danger of a hazard, thus enhancing communication.

OSHA's Hazcom standard will result in all the substance-specific health standards making reference to the HCS and would remove the specific language that must be included on a label for raw materials, mixtures, and products. Currently, OSHA substance-specific standards are inconsistent in that some have their own hazard communication requirements while others reference the HCS and still others are silent, but still are covered by HCS. The new paragraph will reference the modified HCS in each substance specific standard will say the following:

> The employer will include (insert name of chemical) in the hazard communication program to comply with the HCS. The employer will ensure that each employee has access to labels and containers of (insert name of chemical) and safety data sheets, and is trained with the provisions of HCS. The employer will provide information on at least the following hazards: (insert hazards).

Requiring standards to reference HCS will ensure consistency with the GHS revisions and consistency among the standards, and consistency when the specific chemical is part of a mixture. Removal of the current specific warning language is essential for adoption of the GHS language. To leave these provisions in the standards would result in the situation of two potentially conflicting requirements, only one of which (the reference to HCS) would be in accord with the GHS modifications.

Moreover, the hazard statements specified for the chemical in the standard may no longer be correct when the chemical is part of the mixture. As for the standards that now simply reference HCS, labeling will no longer be performance-oriented where producers and employers could choose any language and format that conveyed the necessary information. The GHS revision to HCS requires specific GHS elements, including pictograms, hazard and precautionary statements and signal words on labels.

The following OSHA Standards will be affected by the revised Hazard Communication Standard:

GENERAL INDUSTRY STANDARDS	Part 29 CFR 1910
Asbestos	1910.1001
13 Carcinogens	1910.1003
Vinyl Chloride	1910.1017
Inorganic Arsenic	1910.1018
Lead	1910.1025
Chromium (VI)	1910.1026
Benzene	1910.1028
Coke Oven Emissions	1910.1029
Cotton Dust	1910.1043
1,2-dibromo-3-chloropropane	1910.1044
Acrylonitrile	1910.1045
Ethylene Oxide	1910.1047
Formaldehyde	1910.1048
Methylenedianiline	1910.1050
1,3-Butadiene	1910.1051
Hazard Communication	1910.1200

CONSTRUCTION INDUSTRY STANDARDS	Part 29 CFR 1926
Hazard Communication	1926.59
Methylenedianiline	1926.60
Lead	1926.62
Asbestos	1926.1101
13 Carcinogens (4-Nitrobipheny).	1926.1103
Vinyl Chloride	1926.1117
Inorganic Arsenic	1926.1118
Chromium (VI)	1926.1126
Cadmium	1926.1127
Benzene	1926.1128
Coke Oven Emissions	1926.1129
1,2-dibromo-3-chloropropane	1926.1144
Acrylonitrile	1926.1145
Ethylene Oxide	1926.1147
Formaldehyde	1926.1148
Methylene Chloride	1926.1152

MARITIME INDUSTRY STANDARDS	Parts 29 CFR 1915, 1917 & 1918
Asbestos	1915.1001
13 Carcinogens	1915.1003
Vinyl Chloride	1915.1017
Inorganic Arsenic	1915.1018
Lead	1915.1025
Chromium (VI)	1915.1026
Cadmium	1915.1027
Benzene	1915.1028
1,2-dibromo-3-chloropropane	1915.1044
Acrylonitrile	1915.1045
Ethylene Oxide	1915.1047
Formaldehyde	1915.1048
Methylenedianiline	1915.1050
Methylene Chloride	1915.1052
Hazard Communication	**1915.1200**
Hazard Communication	**1917.28**
Hazard Communication	**1918.90**

- CHAPTER 2 -

How is the GHS to be applied To Hazcom?

Chapter Highlights:

- **What is Meant by Building Blocks?**
- **What are the New Physical & Health Hazards?**
- **A Comparison of the Old & New Hazard Communication Requirements under the Globally Harmonized System (GHS).**

GHS Classification and Communication elements are the foundation of the new Hazard communication standard to ensure the safe use of chemicals, as below in shown in Figure 2.1. The first two steps in any program to ensure the safe use of chemicals are to identify intrinsic hazard(s) (For example, classification) and then to communicate that information. The design of the GHS communication elements reflects the different needs of various target audiences, such as workers and consumers. To proceed further up the pyramid, some existing national programs also include risk management systems as part of an overall program on the sound management of chemicals.

The general goal of these systems is to minimize exposure, resulting in reduced risk. The systems vary in focus and include activities such as establishing exposure limits, recommending exposure monitoring methods and creating engineering controls. However, the target audiences of such systems are generally limited to workplace settings. With or without formal risk management systems, the GHS is designed to promote the safe use of chemicals.

Figure 2.1

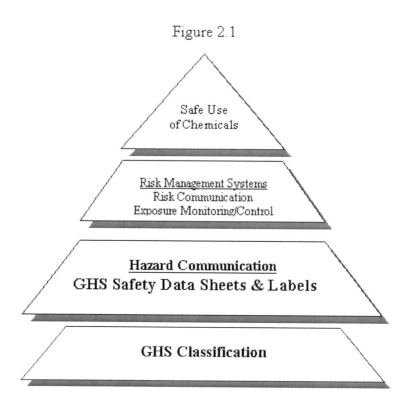

Safe Use
of Chemicals

Risk Management Systems
Risk Communication
Exposure Monitoring/Control

Hazard Communication
GHS Safety Data Sheets & Labels

GHS Classification

Are all Chemicals covered by the GHS?

The GHS covers all hazardous chemicals. There are no complete exemptions from the scope of the GHS for a particular type of chemical or product. The term "chemical" is used broadly to include substances, products, mixtures, preparations, or any other terms that may be used by existing systems. The goal of the GHS is to identify the intrinsic hazards of chemical substances and mixtures and to convey hazard information about these hazards. The GHS is not intended to harmonize risk assessment procedures or risk management decisions, as described above.

Will All Hazardous Chemicals require a GHS Label and Safety Data Sheet?

The need for GHS labels and/or Safety Data Sheets is expected to vary by product category or stage in the chemical's lifecycle from research/production to end use. The sequence of lifecycle events is shown in **Figure 2.2** below. For example, pharmaceuticals, food additives, cosmetics and pesticide residues in food will not be covered by the GHS at the point of consumption, but will be covered where workers may be exposed (workplaces), and in transport.

The medical use of human pharmaceuticals is generally addressed in package inserts and is not part of existing new Hazard communication standard. Similarly, foods are generally not labeled under existing Hazard communication. The exact requirements for labels and Safety Data Sheets will continue to be defined in future regulations.

Figure 2.2

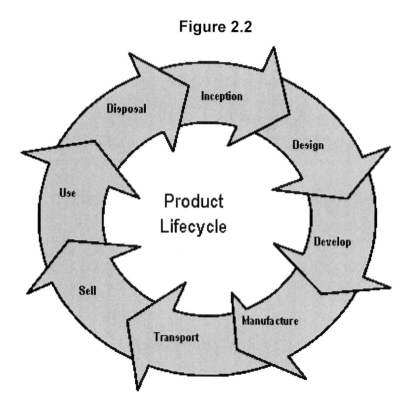

What does a Label look like?

Unlike "open and obvious" physical safety hazards, which may be obvious to the professional, the hazards, consequences, and appropriate procedures for safe use of chemicals cannot be easily determined by looking at the chemical or smelling it. Thus, proper labeling is critical for even the most experienced users.

The HCS currently requires a label on any container of a hazardous chemical under OSHA jurisdiction. "Label" is officially defined as "any written, printed, or graphic material displayed on or affixed to containers of hazardous chemicals" 29 CFR 1910.1200(f) covers label requirements, mandating that the label include the following information:

- **Identity of the hazardous chemical(s).**
- **Appropriate hazard warnings which provide at least general information regarding the hazards of the chemical(s); and**
- **If the product leaves the workplace, it must also include the name and address of the chemical manufacturer, importer, or other responsible party.**

According to the HCS, signs or other written materials can be used in lieu of labels on individual stationary process containers, so long as the information is accessible, etc. Labels must be legible and in English, although employers may add information in another language if they wish.

Existing systems have labels that look different for the same product. We know that this leads to worker confusion, consumer uncertainty and the need for additional resources to maintain different systems. In the U.S. as well as in other countries, chemical products are regulated by sector/target audience. Different agencies regulate the workplace, consumers, agricultural chemicals and transport. Labels for these sectors/target audiences vary both in the U.S. and globally.

In order to understand the value of the GHS and its benefits to all employers, it is important to look at the different labels for one fictional product. In the U.S. the product, **ToxiFlam**, See (**Figures 2.3, 2.4 & 2.5)** which has a flash point of 120°F, has different labels for different sectors/target audiences. Label examples as seen in the

U.S.A. are shown first, followed by international examples.

USA Examples:

In the U.S., regulatory requirements for workplace labels under the old Hazcom standard were 'performance oriented'. This resulted in a minimum straightforward label that has a product identity, hazard statement and supplier identification See (**Figure 2.3**). Some products can also have additional labeling requirements depending on their end use.

Figure 2.3

ToxiFlam
TOXIC
COMBUSTIBLE LIQUID AND
VAPOR
My Company, My Street, My Town, NJ
00000
Tel. 444 999 9999

However, many companies follow the new ANSI Z129.1 Precautionary Labeling Standard for workplace labeling and often use it also for labeling consumer products. The American National Standards Institute (ANSI) standard includes several label elements that are core to the GHS as well as other helpful elements to assist users in safe handling See **(Figure 2.4)**

Figure 2.4

ToxiFlam

WARNING! HARMFUL IF SWALLOWED, FLAMMABLE LIQUID AND VAPOR

Do not taste or swallow. Do not take internally. Wash thoroughly after handling. Keep away from heat, sparks and flame. Keep container closed. Use only with adequate ventilation.

FIRST AID: If swallowed, do NOT induce vomiting unless directed to do so by medical personnel. Never give anything by mouth to an unconscious person.
In case of Fire, use water fog, dry chemical, CO_2, or alcohol foam. Water may be ineffective.

Flash Point = 120°F. Residue vapor may explode or ignite on ignition; do not cut, drill, grind, or weld on or near the container.

In several countries consumer products are regulated separately from workplace chemicals. In the U.S. the CPSC regulates consumer products. Consumer products have required label elements, but only the signal words are specified. The ANSI labeling standard is often used in developing consumer labels.

Agricultural Chemicals and Pesticides

In many systems, agricultural chemicals often have special label requirements. In the U.S. the EPA is the agency covering these chemicals. A pesticide product with the same hazards as ToxiFlam would have a label developed using FIFRA requirements. FIFRA has requirements for product identity, chemical identity, signal word, hazard statements, and precautionary measures including first aid.

International Example

Many companies do business globally. So in addition to the U.S. regulations, these companies would need to comply with the corresponding regulations in the countries to which they export products. Canada and the EU are two existing systems that were considered in the development of the GHS. To illustrate the differences in labeling, it is interesting to examine an EU label for ToxiFlam.
See (**Figure 2.5**).

European Union Label

Labels in the EU have chemical identity, symbols, and R/S (Risk and Safety) phrases which are hazard statements, precautionary measures and first aid.

Figure 2.5

ToxiFlam KEEP OUT OF THE REACH OF CHILDREN

Harmful If Swallowed.
Flammable.
Keep away from food, drink and animal feeding stuffs.
Wear suitable protective clothing.
If swallowed, seek medical advice immediately and show this Container label. In case of fire, use water, fog, CO_2, or alcohol foam.

My Company, My Street, My Town XX 00000, Tel: 44 22 999 9999

How will the GHS impact existing regulations?

The GHS is a voluntary international system that imposes no binding treaty obligations on countries. To the extent that countries adopt the GHS into their systems, the regulatory changes would be binding for covered industries. For countries with existing systems, it is expected that the GHS components will be applied within the framework/infrastructure of existing hazard communication regulatory schemes. For example, exceptions and exemptions found in existing regulations would not be expected to change.

However, the specific hazard criteria, classification processes, label elements and SDS requirements within an existing regulation will need to be modified to be consistent with the harmonized elements of the GHS. It is anticipated that ALL existing hazard communication systems will need to be changed in order to apply the GHS. For example, in the U.S. EPA and OSHA would be expected to require hazard pictograms/symbols on labels.

Canada and the EU would be expected to adopt the GHS pictograms/symbols instead of those currently in use. OSHA HCS, WHMIS and the EU would all need to change their acute toxicity criteria.

What is meant by GHS Building Blocks?

The GHS classification and communication requirements can be thought of as a collection of building blocks. In regulatory schemes, coverage and communication of hazards vary by the needs of target audiences/sectors. Accordingly, the GHS was designed to contain the hazard endpoints and communication tools necessary for application to known regulatory schemes. The GHS is structured so that the appropriate elements for classification and communication, which address the target audiences, can be selected. The full range of these elements does not have to be adopted. Countries can determine which of the building blocks will be applied in different parts of their systems (consumer, workplace, transport, pesticides, etc.). For example, some options for implementing the GHS include:

- **Not using a GHS class (For example, cancer, hazardous to the aquatic environment);**

- **Not using a GHS category (normally at the beginning or end of a class, For example, Acute Toxicity);**

- **Combining categories (For example, Acute Toxicity and; Skin Corrosion).**

How the GHS Building Blocks should be applied?

Appropriate implementation of the GHS means that the hazards covered by a Competent Authority (CA) are covered consistently with the GHS criteria and requirements. The EPA, Health Canada and OSHA are examples of Competent Authorities. Competent Authorities will decide how to apply the various elements of the GHS based on the CA needs and the needs of target audiences.

When a regulatory scheme covers something that is in the GHS, and implements the GHS, that coverage should be consistent. Once an endpoint and subclasses are selected, as needed, the GHS classification criteria, assigned label elements and SDS provisions should be followed as specified in the GHS. If a regulatory system covers carcinogenicity, for example, it should follow the harmonized classification scheme, the harmonized label elements and, where appropriate, the SDS. See **(Figure 2.6)** it shows some of the hazard endpoint/subcategory and hazard communication building block choices for the transport, workplace, consumer and pesticide sectors.

Figure 2.6

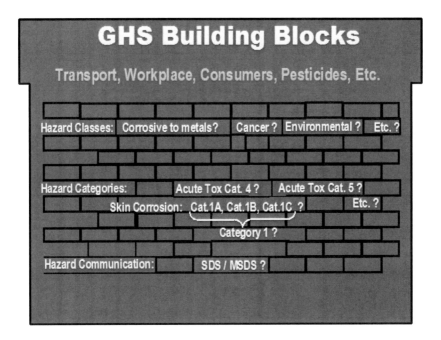

To gain a better understanding of the building block approach, it is helpful to look at the specific sectors/target audiences. The needs and regulations of the various sectors vary depending on the type of chemical and use pattern. Different target audiences or sectors receive and use hazard information in different ways. The primary sectors/target audiences are transport, workplace, consumers and agriculture (pesticides). These sectors are described in more detail below.

Transportation

For transport, it is expected that application of the GHS will be similar to application of current transport requirements.

- **GHS physical, acute and environmental hazard criteria are expected to be adopted in the transport sector.**

- **Containers of dangerous goods will have pictograms that address acute toxicity, physical hazards, and environmental hazards.**

- **GHS hazard communication elements such as signal words, hazard statements and SDS are not expected to be adopted in the transport sector.**

Workplace

In the workplace, it is expected that most of the GHS elements will be adopted, including;

- **GHS physical and health hazard criteria, as appropriate;**

- **Labels that have the harmonized core information under the GHS (signal words, hazard statements and symbols, etc.);**

- **Safety Data Sheets;**

- **Employee training to help ensure effective communication is also anticipated;**

Consumer

For the consumer sector, it is expected that labels will be the primary focus of GHS application.

- **The appropriate GHS hazard criteria are expected to be adopted;**

- **These labels will include the core elements of the GHS (signal words, hazard statements and pictograms).**

Pesticides

For pesticides, it is expected that the GHS will be adopted.

- **The appropriate GHS hazard criteria are expected to be adopted;**

- **Pesticide labels will include the core elements of the GHS (signal words, hazard statements and pictograms**).

What does Classification mean?

Classification is the starting point for hazard communication. It involves the identification of the hazard(s) of a chemical or mixture by assigning a category of hazard/danger using defined criteria. The GHS is designed to be consistent and transparent. It draws a clear distinction between classes and categories in order to allow for "self classification". For several hazards the GHS criteria are semi-quantitative or qualitative.

The term **"Hazard Classification"** is used to indicate that only the intrinsic hazardous properties of substances and mixtures are considered and involves the following 3 steps below:

Figure 2.7

1). Identification of relevant data regarding the hazards of a substance or mixture; **2).** Subsequent review of those data to ascertain the hazards associated with the substance or mixture; and **3)** A decision on whether the substance or mixture will be classified as a hazardous substance or mixture and the degree of hazard, where appropriate, by comparison of the data with agreed hazard classification criteria.

What are the GHS Physical Hazards?

The GHS physical hazards criteria are based on the existing criteria used by the UN Model Regulation on the Transport of Dangerous Goods. Therefore, many of the criteria are already being used on a worldwide basis. However, some additions and changes were necessary since the scope of the GHS includes all target audiences. The physical hazards classification process provides specific references to approved test methods and criteria for classification. The GHS physical hazard criteria apply to mixtures. It is assumed that mixtures will be tested for physical hazards. In developing GHS criteria for physical hazards it was necessary to define physical states. In the GHS:

A **gas** is a substance or mixture which at 50°C has a vapor pressure greater than 300 kPa; or is completely gaseous at 20°C and a standard pressure of 101.3 kPa.

A **liquid** is a substance or mixture that is not a gas and which has a melting point or initial melting point of 20°C or less at standard pressure of 101.3 kPa.

A **solid** is a substance or mixture that does not meet the definitions of a liquid or a gas.

The GHS covers physical, health and environmental hazards are listed in (**Figure 2.8).**

Figure 2.8
Physical Hazard

- EXPLOSIVES
- FLAMMABLE GASES
- FLAMMABLE AEROSOLS
- OXIDIZING GASES
- GASES UNDER PRESSURE
- FLAMMABLE LIQUIDS
- FLAMMABLE SOLIDS
- SELF-REACTIVE SUBSTANCES
- PYROPHORIC LIQUIDS
- PYROPHORIC SOLIDS
- SELF-HEATING SUBSTANCES
- SUBSTANCES WHICH IN CONTACT
- WITH WATER EMIT FLAMMABLE
  GASES
- OXIDIZING LIQUIDS
- OXIDIZING SOLIDS
- ORGANIC PEROXIDES
- CORROSIVE TO METALS

Explosives
An explosive substance (or mixture) is a solid or liquid which is in itself capable by chemical reaction of producing gas at such a temperature and pressure and at such a speed as to cause damage to the surroundings

Classification as an explosive and allocation to a division is a 3-step process:

1).Ascertain if the material has explosive effects;

2).Acceptance procedure; and

3).Assignment to one of six hazard divisions.

Pyrotechnic substances are included even when they do not evolve gases. A pyrotechnic substance (or mixture) is designed to produce an effect by heat, light, sound, gas or smoke or a combination of these as the result of non-detonative, self-sustaining, exothermic chemical reactions.

Explosive properties are associated with certain chemical groups that can react to give very rapid increases in temperature or pressure. The GHS provides a screening procedure that is aimed at identifying the presence of such reactive groups and the potential for rapid energy release. If the screening procedure identifies the substance or mixture to be a potential explosive, the acceptance procedure has to be performed.

Flammable Gases

Flammable gas means a gas having a flammable range in air at 20°C and a standard pressure of 101.3 kPa. Substances and mixtures of this hazard class are assigned to one of two hazard categories on the basis of the outcome of the test or calculation method.

Flammable Aerosols

Aerosols are any gas compressed, liquefied or dissolved under pressure within a non-refillable container made of metal, glass or plastic, with or without a liquid, paste or powder. The container is fitted with a release device allowing the contents to be ejected as solid or liquid particles in suspension in a gas, as a foam, paste or powder or in a liquid or gaseous state.

Aerosols should be considered for classification as either a Category 1 or Category 2 Flammable Aerosol if they contain any component classified as flammable according to the GHS criteria for flammable liquids, flammable gases, or flammable solids. Classification is based on:

- Concentration of flammable components;

- Chemical heat of combustion (mainly for transport/storage);

- Results from the foam test (foam aerosols) (mainly for worker/consumer);

- Ignition distance test (spray aerosols) (mainly for worker/consumer);

- Enclosed space test (spray aerosols) (mainly for worker/consumer).

Aerosols are considered:

- Nonflammable, if the concentration of the flammable components $\leq$ 1% and the heat of combustion is < 20 kJ/g.

- Extremely flammable, if the concentration of the flammable components >85% and the heat of combustion is $\geq$ 30 kJ/g to avoid excessive testing.

- Concentration of flammable components;

- Chemical heat of combustion (mainly for transport/storage);

- Results from the foam test (foam aerosols) (mainly for worker/consumer);

- Ignition distance test (spray aerosols) (mainly for worker/consumer);

- Enclosed space test (spray aerosols) (mainly for worker/consumer).

Oxidizing Gases

Oxidizing gas means any gas which may, generally by providing oxygen, cause or contribute to the combustion of other material more than air does. Substances and mixtures of this hazard class are assigned to a single hazard category on the basis that, generally by providing oxygen, they cause or contribute to the combustion of other material more than air does. Currently, several workplace hazard communication systems cover oxidizers (solids, liquids, gases) as a class of chemicals.

Gases under Pressure

Gases under pressure are gases that are contained in a receptacle at a pressure not less than 280 Pa at 20°C or as a refrigerated liquid. This endpoint covers four types of gases or gaseous mixtures to address the effects of sudden release of pressure or freezing which may lead to serious damage to people, property, or the environment independent of other hazards the gases may pose. Criteria that use the physical state or compressed gases will be a different classification basis for some workplace systems Gases are classified, according to their physical state when packaged, into one of four groups as shown below:

Gases under Pressure Figure 2.9

Group	Criteria
Compressed gas	Entirely gaseous at -50°C
Liquefied gas	Partially liquid at temperatures > -50°C
Refrigerated liquefied gas	Partially liquid because of its low temperature
Dissolved gas	Dissolved in a liquid phase solvent

Flammable Liquids

Flammable liquid means a liquid having a flash point of not more than 93°C. Substances and mixtures of this hazard class are assigned to one of four hazard categories on the basis of the flash point and boiling point **(Figure 3.0)**. Flash Point is determined by closed cup methods.

Flammable Liquids Figure 3.0

Category	Criteria
1	Flash point < 23°C and initial boiling point ≤ 35°C (95°F)
2	Flash point < 23°C and initial boiling point > 35°C (95°F)
3	Flash point ≥ 23°C and ≤ 60°C (140°F)
4	Flash point ≥ 60°C (140°F) and ≤ 93°C (200°F)

Flammable Solids

Flammable solids are solids that are readily combustible, or may cause or contribute to fire through friction. Readily combustible solids are powdered, granular, or pasty substances which are dangerous if they can be easily ignited by brief contact with an ignition source, such as a burning match, and if the flame spreads rapidly.

A Comparison of Hazard Communication Requirements. OSHA Hazard Communication Standard 29 CFR 1910.1200(HCS) & Globally Harmonized System (GHS).

The Globally Harmonized System (GHS) is not in itself a regulation or a model regulation. It is a framework from which competent authorities may select the appropriate harmonized classification & communication elements. Competent authorities will decide how to apply the various elements of the GHS within their systems based on their needs and the target audience.

The harmonized elements of the GHS may be seen as a collection of building blocks from which to form a regulatory approach. While the full range is available to everyone, and should be used if a country or organization chooses to cover a certain effect when it adopts the GHS, the full range does not have to be adopted.

Competent authorities, such as OSHA, will determine how to implement the elements of the GHS within their systems. This Comparison includes the following:

I. General Comparison of the OLD & NEW Hazard Communication Requirements.

II. Comparison of the NEW Health Hazards.

III. Comparison of the NEW Physical Hazards.

IV. Comparison of the OLD & NEW Label Requirements.

V. NEW Label Examples; and

VI. Comparison of the OLD & NEW MSDS Sheets Requirements.

GENERAL COMPARISON
Comparison -The purpose of the HCS and GHS are very consistent. The HCS is one of the major existing systems which are to be harmonized by the GHS. While the intent of the GHS in international harmonization, it will also address harmonization of sectors and regulations within countries.

Old –HCS—29 CFR 1910.1200	NEW – GHS – The Globally Harmonized System for Hazard Communication.
Purpose The purpose of this section is to ensure that the hazards of all chemicals produced or imported are evaluated, and that information concerning their hazards is transmitted to employers and employees. This transmittal of information is to be accomplished by means of comprehensive hazard communication programs, which are to include container labeling and other forms of warning, material safety data sheets and employee training. This occupational safety and health standard is intended to address comprehensively the issue of evaluating the potential hazards of chemicals, and communicating information concerning hazards and appropriate protective	**Purpose** The use of chemical products to enhance and improve life is a widespread practice worldwide. But alongside the benefits of these products, there is also the potential for adverse effects to people or the environment. As a result, a number of countries or organizations have developed laws or regulations over the years that require information to be prepared and transmitted to those using chemicals, through labels or Safety Data Sheets (SDS). Given the large number of chemical products available, individual regulation of all of them is simply not possible for any entity. Provision of information gives those using chemicals the identities and hazards of these chemicals, and allows the appropriate protective measures to be implemented in the local use settings. While these existing regulations are similar in many respects, their differences are significant enough to result in different labels or SDS for the same product in different countries .Through variations in definitions of hazards, a chemical may be considered flammable in one country, but

measures to employees, and to preempt any legal requirements of a state, or political subdivision of a state, pertaining to this subject. Evaluating the potential hazards of chemicals, and communicating information concerning hazards and appropriate protective measures to employees, may include, for example, but is not limited to, provisions for: developing and maintaining a written hazard communication program for the workplace, including lists of hazardous chemicals present; labeling of containers of chemicals in the workplace, as well as of containers of chemicals being shipped to other workplaces; preparation and distribution of material safety data sheets to employees and downstream employers; and development and implementation of employee training programs regarding hazards of chemicals and protective measures. Under section 18 of the Act, no state or political subdivision of a state may adopt or enforce, through any court or agency, any requirement relating to the issue addressed by this Federal standard, except pursuant to a Federally-approved state plan.

not another. Or it may be considered to cause cancer in one country, but not another. Decisions on when or how to communicate hazards on a label or SDS thus vary around the world, and companies wishing to be involved in international trade must have large staffs of experts who can follow the changes in these laws and regulations and prepare different labels and SDS. In addition, given the complexity of developing and maintaining a comprehensive system for classifying and labeling chemicals, many countries have no system at all.

Given the reality of the extensive global trade in chemicals, and the need to develop national programs to ensure their safe use, transport, and disposal, it was recognized that an internationally-harmonized approach to classification and labeling would provide the foundation for such programs. Once countries have consistent and appropriate information on the chemicals they import or produce in their own countries, the infrastructure to control chemical exposures and protect people and the environment can be established in a comprehensive manner.

It is anticipated that, when implemented, the GHS will do the following:

(a) Enhance the protection of human health and the environment by providing an internationally comprehensible system for hazard communication;

(b) Provide are recognized framework for those countries without an existing system;

	(c) Reduce the need for testing and evaluation of chemicals; and
	(d) Facilitate international trade in chemicals whose hazards have been properly assessed and identified on an international basis.
	The work began with examination of existing systems, and determination of the scope of the work. While many countries had some requirements, the following systems were deemed to be the "major" existing systems and were used as the primary basis for the elaboration of the GHS:
	Requirements of systems in the United States of America for the workplace, consumers and pesticides;
	(b) Requirements of Canada for the workplace, consumers and pesticides;
	(c) European Union directives for classification and labeling of substances and preparations;
	(d) The United Nations Recommendations on the Transport of Dangerous Goods. The requirements of other countries were also examined as the work developed, but the primary task was to find ways to adopt the best aspects of these existing systems and develop a harmonized approach. This work was done based on agreed principles of harmonization that were adopted early in the process:

	(a) The level of protection offered to workers, consumers, the general public and the environment should not be reduced as a result of harmonizing the classification and labeling systems;
	(b) The hazard classification process refers principally to the hazards arising from the intrinsic properties of chemical elements and compounds and mixtures thereof, whether natural or synthetic;
	(c) Harmonization means establishing a common and coherent basis for chemical hazard classification and communication, from which the appropriate elements relevant to means of transport, consumer, worker and environment protection can be selected;
	(d) The scope of harmonization includes both hazard classification criteria and hazard communication tools, e.g. labeling and chemical safety data sheets, taking into account especially the four existing systems identified in the ILO report;
	(e) Changes in all these systems will be required to achieve a single globally harmonized system; transitional measures should be included in the process of moving to the new system;
	(f) The involvement of concerned international organizations of employers, workers, consumers, and other relevant organizations in the process of harmonization should be ensured;

	(g) The comprehension of chemical hazard information, by the target audience, e.g. workers, consumers and the general public should be addressed; **(h)** Validated data already generated for the classification of chemicals under the existing systems should be accepted when reclassifying these chemicals under the harmonized system; **(i)** A new harmonized classification system may require adaptation of existing methods for testing of chemicals; **(j)** In relation to chemical hazard communication, the safety and health of workers, consumers and the public in general, as well as the protection of the environment, should be ensured while protecting confidential business information, as prescribed by the competent authorities.

SCOPE
Comparison -The NEW GHS scope is consistent with the HCS exemptions and labeling exceptions. Consumer products and pharmaceuticals are specifically addressed in the NEW GHS SCOPE. The HCS includes laboratories, sealed containers and distributors while as a framework for systems the GHS does not include these specific issues. The NEW GHS addresses testing in the scope section. The OLD HCS addresses testing under hazard determination. The NEW GHS and HCS do not require testing for health hazards.

OLD –HCS – 29 CFR 1910.1200	NEW – GHS - The Globally Harmonized System for Hazard Communication.
29 CFR 1910.1200 (b) Scope and application: This section requires chemical manufacturers or importers to assess the hazards of chemicals which they produce or import, and employers to provide information to their employees about the hazardous chemicals to which they are exposed, by means of a hazard communication program, labels and other forms of warning, material safety data sheets, and information and training. In addition, this section requires distributors to transmit the required information to employers. (Employers who do not produce or import chemicals need only focus on those parts of this rule that deal with establishing a workplace program and communicating information to their workers.	The GHS includes the following: **(a)** Harmonized criteria for classifying substances and mixtures according to their health, environmental and physical hazards; and **(b**) Harmonized hazard communication elements, including requirements for labeling and safety data sheets. This document describes the classification criteria and the hazard communication elements by type of hazard (e.g. acute toxicity; flammability). In addition, decision logics for each hazard have been developed. Some examples of classification of chemicals in the text, illustrate how to apply the criteria. There is also some discussion about

(b)(2)-This section applies to any chemical which is known to be present in the workplace in such a manner that employees may be exposed under normal conditions of use or in a foreseeable emergency.

(b)(3)-This section applies to laboratories only as follows:

(b)(3)(i)-Employers shall ensure that labels on incoming containers of hazardous chemicals are not removed or defaced;

Employers shall maintain any material safety data sheets that are received with incoming shipments of hazardous chemicals, and ensure that they are readily accessible during each work shift to laboratory employees when they are in their work areas;

(b)(3)(iii)-Employers shall ensure that laboratory employees are provided information and training in accordance with

paragraph (h) of this section, except for the location and availability of the written hazard communication program under paragraph(h)(2)(iii) of this section; and,

(b)(3)(iv)-Laboratory employers that ship hazardous chemicals reconsidered to be either a chemical manufacturer or a distributor under this

issues that were raised during the development of the system where additional guidance was thought to be necessary to implement the system.

The scope of the GHS is based on the mandate from the 1992 United Nations Conference on Environment and Development (UNCED) for development of such a system reproduced below:

Globally harmonized hazard classification and labeling systems are not yet available to promote the safe use of chemicals, inter alia, at the workplace or in the home. Classification of chemicals can be made for different purposes and is a particularly important tool in establishing labeling systems. There is a need to develop harmonized hazard classification and labeling systems, building on ongoing work;

A globally harmonized hazard classification and compatible labeling system, including material safety data sheets and easily understandable symbols, should be available, by the year 2000."

rule, and thus must ensure that any containers of hazardous chemicals leaving the laboratory are labeled in accordance with paragraph (f)(1) of this section, and that a material safety data sheet is provided to distributors and other employers in accordance with paragraphs (g)(6) and (g)(7) of this section

(b)(4)-In work operations where employees only handle chemicals in sealed containers which are not opened under normal conditions of use (such as are found in marine cargo handling, warehousing, or retail sales), this section applies to these operations only as follows:

(b)(4)(i)-Employers shall ensure that labels on incoming containers of hazardous chemicals are not removed or defaced;

(b)(4)(ii)-Employers shall maintain copies of any material safety data sheets that are received with incoming shipments of the sealed containers of hazardous chemicals, shall obtain a material safety data sheet as soon as possible for sealed containers of hazardous chemicals received without a material safety data sheet if an employee requests the material safety data sheet, and shall ensure that the material safety data sheets are readily accessible during each work shift to employees when they are in their work area(s); and,

This mandate was later analyzed and refined in the harmonization process to identify the parameters of the GHS. As a result, the following clarification was adopted by the Interorganization Program for the Sound Management of Chemicals (IOMC) Coordinating Group to ensure that participants were aware of the scope of the effort:

"The work on harmonization of hazard classification and labeling focuses on a harmonized system for all chemicals, and mixtures of chemicals. The application of the components of the system may vary by type of product or stage of the life cycle. Once a chemical is classified, the likelihood of adverse effects may be considered in deciding what informational or other steps should be taken for a given product or use setting. Pharmaceuticals, food additives, cosmetics, and pesticide residues in food will not be covered by the GHS in terms of labeling at the point of intentional intake. However, these types of chemicals would be covered where workers may be exposed, and, in transport if potential exposure warrants. The Coordinating Group for the Harmonization of Chemical Classification Systems (CG/HCCS) recognizes that

(b)(4)(iii)-Employers shall ensure that employees are provided with information and training in accordance with paragraph (h) of this section (except for the location and availability of the written hazard communication program under paragraph (h)(2)(iii) of this section), to the extent necessary to protect them in the event of a spill or leak of a hazardous chemical from a sealed container.

(b)(5)-This section does not require labeling of the following chemicals:

(b)(5)(i)-Any pesticide as such term is defined in the Federal Insecticide, Fungicide, and Rodenticide Act (7 U.S.C. 136 et seq.), when subject to the labeling requirements of that Act and labeling regulations issued under that Act by the Environmental Protection Agency;

(b)(5)(ii)-Any chemical substance or mixture as such terms redefined in the Toxic Substances Control Act (15 U.S.C. 2601 et seq.), when subject to the labeling requirements of that Act and labeling regulations issued under that Act by the Environmental Protection Agency;

(b)(5)(iii)-Any food, food additive, color additive, drug, cosmetic, or medical or veterinary device or product, including materials intended for use as

further discussion will be required to address specific application issues for some product use categories which may require the use of specialized expertise.

In developing this clarification, the CG/HCCS carefully considered many different issues with regard to the possible application of the GHS. There were concerns raised about whether certain sectors or products should be exempted, for example, or about whether or not the system would be applied at all stages of the life cycle of a chemical. Three parameters were agreed in this discussion, and are critical to application of the system in a country or region. These are described below:

a) Parameter : The GHS covers all hazardous chemicals. The mode of application of the hazard communication components of the GHS (e.g. labels, safety data sheets) may vary by product category or stage in the life cycle. Target audiences for the GHS include consumers, workers, transport workers, and emergency responders

(i) Existing hazard classification and labeling systems address potential exposures to all potentially hazardous chemicals in all types of use situations, including production, storage,

ingredients in such products (e.g. flavors and fragrances), as such terms are defined in the Federal Food, Drug, and Cosmetic Act (21 U.S.C. 301et seq.) or the Virus-Serum-Toxin Act of 1913 (21 U.S.C. 151 et seq.), and regulations issued under those Acts, when they are subject to the labeling requirements under those Acts by either the Food and Drug Administration or the Department of Agriculture;

(b)(5)(iv)-Any distilled spirits (beverage alcohols), wine, or malt beverage intended for non industrial use, as such terms are defined in the Federal Alcohol Administration Act (27 U.S.C. 201 et seq.) and regulations issued under that Act, when subject to the labeling requirements of that Act and labeling regulations issued under that Act by the Bureau of Alcohol, Tobacco, and Firearms;

(b)(5)(v)-Any consumer product or hazardous substance as those terms are defined in the Consumer Product Safety Act (15 U.S.C. 2051 et seq.) and Federal Hazardous Substances Act (15 U.S.C. 1261 et seq.) respectively, when subject to a consumer product safety standard or labeling requirement of those Acts, or regulations issued under those Acts by the Consumer Product Safety Commission; and,

(b)(5)(vi)-Agricultural or vegetable seed treated with pesticides and labeled in accordance with the Federal

transport, workplace use, consumer use, and presence in the environment. They are intended to protect people, facilities, and the environment. The most widely applied requirements in terms of chemicals covered are generally found in the parts of existing systems that apply to the workplace or transport. It should be noted that the term chemical is used broadly in the UNCED agreements and subsequent documents to include substances, products, mixtures, preparations, or any other terms that may be used in existing systems to denote coverage.

(ii) Since all chemicals and chemical products in commerce are made in a workplace (including consumer products), handled during shipment and transport by workers, and often used by workers, there are no complete exemptions from the scope of the GHS for any particular type of chemical or product. In some countries, for example, pharmaceuticals are currently covered by workplace and transport requirements in the manufacturing, storage, and transport stages of the life cycle. Workplace requirements may also be applied to employees involved in the administration of some drugs, or clean-up of spills and other types of potential

Seed Act (7 U.S.C. 1551 et seq.) and the labeling regulations issued under that Act by the Department of Agriculture.

(b)(6)-This section does not apply to:

(b)(6)(i)-Any hazardous waste as such term is defined by the Solid Waste Disposal Act, as amended by the Resource Conservation and Recovery Act of 1976, as amended (42 U.S.C. 6901 et seq.), when subject to regulations issued under that Act by the Environmental Protection Agency;

(b)(6)(ii)-Any hazardous substance as such term is defined by the Comprehensive Environmental Response, Compensation and Liability ACT (CERCLA)(42 U.S.C. 9601 et seq.) when the hazardous substance is the focus of remedial or removal action being conducted under CERCLA in accordance with the Environmental Protection Agency regulations.

(b)(6)(iii)-Tobacco or tobacco products;

(b)(6)(iv)-Wood or wood products, including lumber which will not be processed, where the chemical manufacturer or importer can establish that the only hazard they pose to employees is the potential for flammability or combustibility (wood or

exposures in health care settings. SDSs and training must be available for these employees under some systems. It is anticipated that the GHS would be applied to pharmaceuticals in a similar fashion.

(iii) At other stages of the life cycle for these same products, the GHS may not be applied at all. For example, at the point of intentional human intake or ingestion, or intentional application to animals, products such as human or veterinary pharmaceuticals are generally not subject to hazard labeling under existing systems. Such requirements would not normally be applied to these products as a result of the GHS. (It should be noted that the risks to subjects associated with the medical use of human or veterinary pharmaceuticals are generally addressed in package inserts and are not part of this harmonization process.) Similarly, products such as foods that may have trace amounts of food additives or pesticides in them are not currently labeled to indicate the presence or hazard of those materials. It is anticipated that application of the GHS would not require them to be labeled as such.

wood products which have been treated with a hazardous chemical covered by this standard, and wood which may be subsequently sawed or cut, generating dust, are not exempted);

(b)(6)(v)-Articles (as that term is defined in paragraph (c) of this section);

(b)(6)(vi)-Food or alcoholic beverages which are sold, used, or prepared in a retail establishment (such as a grocery store, restaurant, or drinking place), and foods intended for personal consumption by employees while in the workplace;

(b)(6)(vii)-Any drug, as that term is defined in the Federal Food, Drug, and Cosmetic Act (21 U.S.C. 301 et seq.), when it is in solid, final form for direct administration to the patient (e.g., tablets or pills); drugs which are packaged by the chemical manufacturer for sale to consumers in a retail establishment (e.g., over-the-counter drugs); and drugs intended for personal consumption by employees while in the workplace (e.g., first aid supplies);

(b)(6)(viii)-Cosmetics which are packaged for sale to consumers in a retail establishment, and cosmetics intended for personal consumption by employees while in the workplace;

(b)(6)(ix)-Any consumer product or hazardous substance, as those terms

b) Parameter 2: The mandate for development of a GHS does not include establishment of uniform test methods or promotion of further testing to address adverse health outcomes.

(i) Tests that determine hazardous properties, which are conducted according to internationally recognized scientific principles, can be used for purposes of a hazard determination for health and environmental hazards. The GHS criteria for determining health and environmental hazards are test method neutral, allowing different approaches as long as they are scientifically sound and validated according to international procedures and criteria already referred to in existing systems for the hazard class of concern and produce mutually acceptable data. While the

OECD is the lead organization for development of harmonized health hazard criteria, the GHS is not tied to the OECD Test Guidelines Program. For example, drugs are tested according to agreed criteria developed under the auspices of the World Health Organization (WHO). Data generated in accordance with these tests would be acceptable under the

are defined in the Consumer Product Safety Act (15 U.S.C. 2051 et seq.) and Federal Hazardous Substances Act (15 U.S.C. 1261 et seq.) respectively, where the employer can show that it is used in the workplace for the purpose intended by the chemical manufacturer or importer of the product, and the use results in a duration and frequency of exposure which is not greater than the range of exposures that could reasonably be experienced by consumers when used for the purpose intended.	GHS. Criteria for physical hazards under the UNSCETDG are linked to specific test methods for hazard classes such as flammability and explosivity. **(ii)** The GHS is based on currently available data. Since the harmonized classification criteria are developed on the basis of existing data, compliance with these criteria will not require retesting of chemicals for which accepted test data already exists. **(c) Parameter 3:** In addition to animal data and valid in vitro testing, human experience, epidemiological data, and clinical testing provide important information that should be considered in application of the GHS. Most of the current systems acknowledge and make use of ethically obtained human data or available human experience. Application of the GHS should not prevent the use of such data, and the GHS explicitly acknowledges the existence and use of all appropriate and relevant information concerning hazards or the likelihood of harmful effects (i.e. risk).

APPLICATION
Comparison -The NEW GHS will require decisions concerning the application of the building blocks for physical and health hazard classes and hazard categories which the OLD HCS does not have.

OLD -HCS -29 CFR 1910.1200	NEW –GHS - The Globally Harmonized System for Hazard Communication.
The HCS is a performance -- oriented regulation. The GHS is a specification oriented. Implementation of the GHS will require changes to the performance-oriented nature of the HCS. These changes will include required label elements and a required MSDS format, as well as criteria changes. Changes to the HCS are expected. The HCS may not implement all hazard classes, e.g., hazardous for the environment. Even within some hazard classes the HCS may not regulate all hazard categories, e.g., acute toxicity. Many hazard classes will require some type of change to the HCS.	The goal of the GHS is to identify the intrinsic hazards found in chemical substances and mixtures and to convey hazard information about these hazards. The criteria for hazard classification are harmonized. Hazard statements, symbols and signal words have been standardized and harmonized and now foreman integrated hazard communication system. The GHS will allow the hazard communication elements of the existing systems to converge. Competent authorities will decide how to apply the various elements of the GHS based on the needs of the competent authority and the target audience. For transport, it is expected that application of the GHS will be similar to application of current transport requirements. Containers of dangerous goods will be marked with pictograms that address acute toxicity, physical hazards, and environmental hazards. As is true for workers in other sectors workers in the transport sector will be trained. The elements of the GHS that address such elements as signal word sand hazard statements are not

	expected to be adopted in the transport sector.
	In the workplace, it is expected that all of the GHS elements will be adopted, including labels that have the harmonized core information under the GHS, and safety data sheets. It is also anticipated that this will be supplemented by employee training to help ensure effective communication.
	For the consumer sector, it is expected that labels will be the primary focus of GHS application. These labels will include the core elements of the GHS, subject to some sector-specific considerations in certain systems.
	Building Block Approach -Consistent with the building block approach, countries are free to determine which of the building blocks will be applied in different parts of their systems. However, where a system covers something that is in the GHS, and implements the GHS, that coverage should be consistent. For example, if a system covers the carcinogenicity of a chemical, it should follow the harmonized classification scheme and the harmonized label elements.
	In examining the requirements of existing systems, it was noted that coverage of hazards may vary by the perceived needs of the target audience for information. In particular, the transport sector focuses on acute health effects and physical hazards, but has not to date covered chronic effects

| | due to the types of exposures expected to be encountered in that setting. But there may be other differences as well, with countries choosing not to cover all of the effects addressed by the GHS in each use setting. |
| | The harmonized elements of the GHS may thus be seen as a collection of building blocks from which to form a regulatory approach. While the full range is available to everyone, and should be used if a country or organization chooses to cover a certain effect when it adopts the GHS, the full range does not have to be adopted. While physical hazards are important in the workplace and transport sectors, consumers may not need to know some of the specific physical hazards in the type of use they have for a product. As long as the hazards covered by a sector or system are covered consistently with the GHS criteria and requirements, it will be considered appropriate implementation of the GHS. Notwithstanding the fact that an exporter needs to comply with importing countries GHS implementation, it is hoped that the application of the GHS worldwide will eventually lead to a fully harmonized situation. |

DEFINITIONS	
Comparison - The NEW GHS has added some new definitions. For example, Hazard Statement, Signal Word, Precautionary Statement, and Pictograms are some major differences. The GHS also has criteria for physical hazards.	
OLD -HCS – 29 CFR 1910.1200 **(c) Definitions**	**NEW –GHS- The Globally Harmonized System for Hazard Communication.** **Definitions and abbreviations:**
"Chemical" means any element, chemical compound or mixture of elements and/or compounds.	Substance means chemical elements and their compounds in the natural state or obtained by any production process, including any additive necessary to preserve the stability of the product and any impurities deriving from the process used, but excluding any solvent which may be separated without affecting the stability of the substance or changing its composition;
"Chemical name" means the scientific designation of a chemical in accordance with the nomenclature system developed by the International Union of Pure and Applied Chemistry (IUPAC) or the Chemical Abstracts Service (CAS) rules of nomenclature, or a name which will clearly identify the chemical for the purpose of conducting a hazard evaluation. "Specific chemical identity" means the chemical name, Chemical	Chemical identity means a name that will uniquely identify a chemical. This can be a name that is in accordance with the nomenclature systems of the International Union of Pure and Applied Chemistry (IUPAC) or the Chemical Abstracts Service (CAS), or a technical name;

Abstracts Service (CAS) Registry Number, or any other information that reveals the precise chemical designation of the substance.	
"Combustible liquid" means any liquid having a flagship at or above 100 deg. F (37.8 deg. C), but below 200 deg. F (93.3deg. C), except any mixture having components with flash points of 200 deg. F(93.3 deg. C), or higher, the total volume of which make up 99 percent or more of the total volume of the mixture.	See flammable liquid hazard categories.
"Common name" means any designation or identification such as code name, code number, trade name, brand name or generic name used to identify a chemical other than by its chemical name.	No GHS definition
"Compressed gas" means: (i) A gas or mixture of gases having, in a container, an absolute pressure exceeding 40 psi at 70 deg. F (21.1 deg. C); or (ii) A gas or mixture of gases having, in a container, an absolute pressure exceeding 104 psi at 130 deg. F (54.4 deg. C) regardless of the pressure at 70 deg. F (21.1 deg. C); or (iii) A liquid having a vapor pressure exceeding 40 psi at100 deg. F (37.8 deg. C) as determined	"Compressed gas": A gas which when packaged under pressure is entirely gaseous at -50 °C; including all gases with a critical temperature $\leq$-50 °C.

by ASTM D-323-72.	
No HCS definition.	Corrosive to metal means a substance or a mixture which by chemical action will materially damage, or even destroy, metals;
"Explosive" means a chemical that causes a sudden, almost instantaneous release of pressure, gas, and heat when subjected to sudden shock, pressure, or high temperature.	Explosive article means an article containing one or more explosive substances; Explosive substance means a solid or liquid substance (or mixture of substances) which is in itself capable by chemical reaction of producing gas at such a temperature and pressure and at such a speed as to cause damage to the surroundings. Pyrotechnic substances are included even when they do not evolve gases;
"Flammable" means a chemical that falls into one of the following categories: (i) "Aerosol, flammable" means an aerosol that, when tested by the method described in 16 CFR 1500.45, yields a flame projection exceeding 18 inches at full valve opening, or a flashback (a flame extending back to the valve) at any degree of valve opening; (ii) "Gas, flammable" means: (A) A gas that, at ambient temperature and pressure, forms a flammable mixture with air at a concentration of thirteen (13) percent by volume or less; or	"Flammable gas": A gas having a flammable range with air at 20 C and a standard pressure of 101.3 kPa. "Flammable Liquid": A flammable liquid means a liquid having a flash point of not more than93 C. "Flammable Solid": A flammable solid is a solid which is readily combustible, or may cause or contribute to fire through friction. "Aerosols" means any non-refillable receptacles made of metal, glass or plastics and containing a gas compressed, liquefied or dissolved under pressure, with or without a liquid, paste or powder, and fitted with a release device allowing the

(B) A gas that, at ambient temperature and pressure, forms a range of flammable mixtures with air wider than twelve (12) percent by volume, regardless of the lower limit;	contents to be ejected as solid or liquid particles in suspension in a gas, as a foam, paste or powder or in a liquid state or in a gaseous state. Aerosol includes aerosol dispensers;
(iii) "Liquid, flammable" means any liquid having a flashpoint below 100 deg. F (37.8 deg. C), except any mixture having components with flash points of 100 deg. F (37.8 deg. C) or higher, the total of which make up 99 percent or more of the total volume of the mixture.	"Readily Combustible Solid": Readily combustible solids are powdered, granular, or pasty substances which are dangerous if they can be easily ignited by brief contact with an ignition source, such as a burning match, and if the flame spreads rapidly.
(iv) "Solid, flammable" means a solid, other than a blasting agent or explosive as defined in 1910.109(a), that is liable to cause fire through friction, absorption of moisture, spontaneous chemical change, or retained heat from manufacturing or processing, or which can be ignited readily and when ignited burns so vigorously and persistently as to create a serious hazard. A chemical shall be considered to be a flammable solid if, when tested by the method described in 16 CFR 1500.44, it ignites and burns with a self-sustained flame at a rate greater than one-tenth of an inch per second along its major axis.	
"Flashpoint" means the minimum temperature at which a liquid gives off a vapor in sufficient concentration to ignite when tested as follows:	"Flash point" means the lowest temperature (corrected to a standard pressure of 101.3 kPa) at which the application of an ignition source causes the vapors of a liquid to ignite

	under specified test conditions;
(i) Tagliabue Closed Tester (See American National Standard Method of Test for Flash Point by Tag Closed Tester, Z11.24-1979(ASTM D 56-79)) for liquids with a viscosity of less than 45 Saybolt Universal Seconds (SUS) at 100 deg. F (37.8 deg. C), that do not contain suspended solids and do not have a tendency to form a surface film under test; or (ii) Pensky-Martens Closed Tester (see American National Standard Method of Test for Flash Point by Pensky-Martens Closed Tester,Z11.7-1979 (ASTM D 93-79)) for liquids with a viscosity equal to or greater than 45 SUS at 100 deg. F (37.8 deg. C), or that contain suspended solids, or that have a tendency to form a surface film under test; or (iii) Setaflash Closed Tester (see American National Standard Method of Test for Flash Point by Setaflash Closed Tester (ASTM D3278-78)).	
No HCS definition	Gas means a substance which (i) at50 °C has a vapor pressure greater than 300 kPa; or (ii) is completely gaseous at 20 °C at a standard pressure of 101.3 kPa; Dissolved gas means a gas which when packaged under pressure is dissolved in a liquid phase solvent;

	Liquefied gas means a gas which when packaged under pressure, is partially liquid at temperatures above -50 °C. A distinction is made between:
	(i) High pressure liquefied gas: a gas with a critical temperature between -50 °C and +65°C; and (ii) Low pressure liquefied gas: a gas with a critical temperature above +65 °C;
	"Refrigerated liquefied gas": A gas which when packaged is made partially liquid because of its low temperature.
"Health hazard" means a chemical for which there is statistically significant evidence based on at least one study conducted in accordance with established scientific principles that acute or chronic health effects may occur in exposed employees. The term "health hazard" includes chemicals which are carcinogens, toxic or highly toxic agents, reproductive toxins, irritants, corrosives, sensitizers, hepatotoxins, nephrotoxins, neurotoxins, agents which act on the hematopoietic system, and agents which damage the lungs, skin, eyes, or mucous membranes. Appendix A provides further definitions and explanations of the scope of health hazards covered by this section, and Appendix B describes the criteria to be used to determine whether or	Hazard category means the division of criteria within each hazard class,. e.g. oral acute toxicity includes five hazard categories and flammable liquids includes four hazard categories. These categories compare hazard severity within a hazard class and should not be taken as a comparison of hazard categories more generally; Hazard class means the nature of the physical, health or environmental hazard, e.g. flammable solid carcinogen, oral acute toxicity;

not a chemical is to be considered hazardous for purposes of this standard. (See appendix for criteria.)	
"Hazard warning" means any words, pictures, symbols, or combination thereof appearing on a label or other appropriate form of warning which convey the specific physical and health hazard(s), including target organ effects, of the chemical(s) in the container(s). (See the definitions for "physical hazard" and "health hazard" to determine the hazards which must be covered.)	**Hazard statement** means a statement assigned to a hazard class and category that describes the nature of the hazards of a hazardous product, including, where appropriate, the degree of hazard; "**Signal word**": A signal word means a word used to indicate the relative level of severity of hazard and alert the reader to a potential hazard on the label. The GHS uses 'Danger' and 'Warning'. "**Pictogram**": A pictogram means a composition that may include a symbol plus other graphic elements, such as a border, background pattern or color that is intended to convey specific information. "**Precautionary statement**": A precautionary statement means a phrase (and/or pictogram) that describes recommended measures that should be taken to minimize or prevent adverse effects resulting from exposure to a hazardous product, or improper storage or handling of a hazardous product.

	"Supplemental Label Element"- A supplemental label element means any additional non-harmonized type of information supplied on the container of a hazardous product that is not required or specified under the GHS. In some cases this information may be required by other competent authorities or it may be additional information provided at the discretion of the manufacturer/distributor. **"Symbol"**-A symbol means a graphical element intended to convey information.
"Label" means any written, printed, or graphic material displayed on or affixed to containers of hazardous chemicals.	**Label means** an appropriate group of written, printed or graphic information elements concerning a hazardous product, selected as relevant to the target sector (s), that is affixed to, printed on, or attached to the immediate container of a hazardous product, or to the outside packaging of a hazardous product; Label element means one type of information that has been harmonized for use in a label, e.g. pictogram, signal word;
No HCS definition	Liquid means a substance or mixture which at 50 °C has a vapor pressure of not more than300 kPa (3 bar), which is not completely gaseous at 20 °C and at a standard pressure of 101.3 kPa, and which has a melting point or initial melting point of 20 °C

	or less at a standard pressure of 101.3 kPa. A viscous substance or mixture for which a specific melting point cannot be determined shall be subjected to the ASTM D 4359-90 test; or to the test for determining fluidity (penetrometer test) prescribed in section 2.3.4 of Annex A of the European Agreement concerning the International Carriage of Dangerous Goods by Road (ADR);
"Mixture" means any combination of two or more chemicals if the combination is not, in whole or in part, the result of a chemical reaction.	Mixture means a mixture or a solution composed of two or more substances in which they do not react; Alloy means a metallic material, homogeneous on a macroscopic scale, consisting of two or more elements so combined that they cannot be readily separated by mechanical means. Alloys are considered to be mixtures for the purpose of classification under the GHS.;
"Oxidizer" means a chemical other than a blasting agent or explosive as defined in 1910.109(a), that initiates or promotes combustion in other materials, thereby causing fire either of itself or through the release of oxygen or other gases.	Oxidizing gas means any gas which may, generally by providing oxygen, cause or contribute to the combustion of other material more than air does; Oxidizing liquid means a liquid which, while in itself not necessarily combustible, may, generally by yielding oxygen, cause, or contribute to, the combustion of other material;

	Oxidizing solid means a solid which, while in itself not necessarily combustible, may, generally by yielding oxygen, cause, or contribute to, the combustion of other material;
"Organic peroxide" means an organic compound that contains the bivalent -O-O-structure and which may be considered to be a structural derivative of hydrogen peroxide where one or both of the hydrogen atoms has been replaced by an organic radical.	Organic peroxide means a liquid or solid organic substance which contains the bivalent -0-0- structure and maybe considered a derivative of hydrogen peroxide, where one or both of the hydrogen atoms have been replaced by organic radicals. The term also includes organic peroxide formulation (mixtures);
"Identity" means any chemical or common name which is indicated on the material safety data sheet (MSDS) for the chemical. The identity used shall permit cross-references to be made among the required list of hazardous chemicals, the label and the MSDS.	**"Product identifier":** A product identifier means the name or number used for a hazardous product on a label or in the SDS. It provides a unique means by which the product user can identify the substance or mixture within the particular use setting e.g. transport, consumer or workplace.
"Pyrophoric" means a chemical that will ignite spontaneously in air at a temperature of 130 deg. F (54.4 deg. C) or below.	"Pyrophoric Liquid": A pyrophoric liquid is a liquid which, even in small quantities, is liable to ignite within five minutes after coming into contact with air. "Pyrophoric Solid": A pyrophoric solid is a solid which, even in small quantities, is liable to ignite within five minutes after coming into contact with air.

	"Pyrotechnic substance": A substance or mixture of substances designed to produce an effect by heat, light, sound, gas or smoke or a combination of these as the result of non-detonative self-sustaining exothermic chemical reactions.
No HCS definition	**"Technical name":** A name that is generally used in commerce, regulations and codes to identify a substance or mixture, other than the IUPAC or CAS name, and that is recognized by the scientific community. Examples of technical names include those used for complex mixtures (e.g., petroleum fractions or natural products), pesticides (e.g., ISO or ANSI systems), dyestuffs (Color Index system) and minerals.
"Trade secret" means any confidential formula, pattern, process, device, information or compilation of information that is used in an employer's business, and that gives the employer an opportunity to obtain an advantage over competitors who do not know or use it. Appendix D sets out the criteria to be used in evaluating trade secrets.	**CBI means** "confidential business information".
"Unstable (reactive)" means a chemical which in the pure state, or as produced or transported, will vigorously polymerize, decompose, condense, or will become self-reactive under conditions of	"Self-Heating Substance": A self-heating substance is a solid or liquid substance, other than a pyrophoric substance, which, by reaction with air and without energy supply, is liable to self-heat; this substance

shocks, pressure or temperature. "Pyrophoric" means a chemical that will ignite spontaneously in air at a temperature of 130 deg. F (54.4 deg. C) or below.	differs from a pyrophoric substance in that it will ignite only when in large amounts (kilograms) and after long periods of time (hours or days).
"Unstable (reactive)" means a chemical which in the pure state, or as produced or transported, will vigorously polymerize, decompose, condense, or will become self-reactive under conditions of shocks, pressure or temperature.	"Self-reactive Substance": Self-reactive substances are thermally unstable liquid or solid substances liable to undergo a strongly exothermic decomposition even without participation of oxygen (air). This definition excludes substances or mixtures classified under the GHS as explosive, organic peroxides or as oxidizing.
"Water-reactive" means a chemical that reacts with water to release a gas that is either flammable or presents a health hazard	"**Substances which,** in contact with water, emit flammable gases" are solid or liquid substances which, by interaction with water, are liable to become spontaneously flammable or to give off flammable gases in dangerous quantities.

HAZARD DETERMINATION/CLASSIFICATION

Comparison -A significant difference between the HCS and GHS is in the evaluation of mixtures. The NEW GHS criteria for mixtures vary by hazard class. The OLD HCS allows test data on mixtures to be used for all hazard classes. The NEW GHS allows test data on carcinogens, mutagens & reproductive toxins on a case-by-case basis. .

OLD- HCS 29 CFR - 1910.12001910.1200 **(d) Hazard Determination**	NEW –GHS - The Globally Harmonized System for Hazard Communication.
(d)(1)-Chemical manufacturers and importers shall evaluate chemicals produced in their work places or imported by them to determine if they are hazardous. Employers are not required to evaluate chemicals unless they choose not to rely on the evaluation performed by the chemical manufacturer or importer for the chemical to satisfy this requirement.	The GHS applies to pure chemical substances, their dilute solutions and to mixtures of chemical substances. "Articles" as defined in the Hazard Communication Standard (29 CFR 1910.1200) of the US Occupational Safety and Health Administration, or by similar definition, are outside the scope of the system.
(d)(2)-Chemical manufacturers, importers or employers evaluating chemicals shall identify and consider the available scientific evidence concerning such hazards. For health hazards, evidence which is statistically significant and which is based on at least one positive study conducted in accordance with established scientific principles is considered to be sufficient to	One objective of the GHS is for it to be simple and transparent with a clear distinction between classes and categories in order to allow for "self classification" as far as possible. For many hazard classes the criteria are semi-quantitative or qualitative and expert judgment is required to interpret the data for classification purposes. Furthermore, for some hazard classes (e.g. eye irritation, explosives or self-reactive substances) a decision tree

establish a hazardous effect if the results of the study meet the definitions of health hazards in this section. Appendix A shall be consulted for the scope of health hazards covered, and Appendix B shall be consulted for the criteria to be followed with respect to the completeness of the evaluation, and the data to be reported.

(d)(3)-The chemical manufacturer, importer or employer evaluating chemicals shall treat the following sources as establishing that the chemicals listed in them are hazardous:

(d)(3)(i)-29CFR part 1910, subpart Z, Toxic and Hazardous Substances, Occupational Safety and Health Administration (OSHA); or,

(d)(3)(ii)-"Threshold Limit Values for Chemical Substances and Physical Agents in the Work Environment," American Conference of Governmental Industrial Hygienists (ACGIH) (latest edition). The chemical manufacturer, importer, or employer is still responsible for evaluating the hazards associated with the chemicals in these source lists.

approach is provided to enhance ease of use.

"Classification"

The GHS uses the term "hazard classification" to indicate that only the intrinsic hazardous properties of substances or mixtures are considered.

Hazard classification means:

(a) Identification of relevant data regarding the hazards of a substance or mixture;

(b) Subsequent review of those data to ascertain the hazards associated with the substance or mixture; and

(c) A decision on whether the substance or mixture will be classified as a hazardous substance or mixture and the degree of hazard, where appropriate, by comparison of the data with agreed hazard classification criteria.

Classification criteria (mixtures):

The classification criteria for substances and mixtures for a specific hazard class or a group of closely related hazard classes. The recommended process of classification of mixtures is based on the following sequence:

(d)(4)-Chemical manufacturers, importers and employers evaluating chemicals shall treat the following sources as establishing that a chemical is a carcinogen or potential carcinogen for hazard communication purposes:

(d)(4)(i)-National Toxicology Program (NTP), "Annual Report on Carcinogens" (latest edition);

(d)(4)(ii)-International Agency for Research on Cancer (IARC) "Monographs" (latest editions); or

(d)(4)(iii)-29 CFR part 1910, subpart Z, Toxic and Hazardous Substances, Occupational Safety and Health Administration.

(d)(5)-The chemical manufacturer, importer or employer shall determine the hazards of mixtures of chemicals as follows:

(d)(5)(i)-If a mixture has been tested as a whole to determine its hazards, the results of such testing shall be used to determine whether the mixture is hazardous;

(d)(5)(ii)-If a mixture has not been tested as a whole to determine whether the mixture is a health hazard, the mixture shall be assumed to present the same health hazards as do the components which comprise one percent (by weight or volume) or greater of the mixture, except that

(a) Where test data are available for the complete mixture, the classification of the mixture will always be based on that data;

(b) Where test data are not available for the mixture itself, then bridging principles included and explained in each specific chapter should be considered to see whether they permit classification of the mixture;

In addition, for the health and environmental classes,

(c) If test data are not available for the mixture itself, and (ii) the available information is not sufficient to allow application of the above mentioned bridging principles, then the agreed method(s) described in each chapter for estimating the hazards based on the information known will be applied to classify the mixture.

Working Group on Physical Hazards

The Working Group for Physical Hazards used a similar process to the OECD Task Force on HCL. The work involved a comparison of the major classification systems, identification of similar or identical elements and for the elements, which were dissimilar, development of a consensus on a compromise. For physical hazards, however, the

the mixture shall be assumed to present a carcinogenic hazard if it contains a component in concentrations of0.1 percent or greater which is considered to be a carcinogen under paragraph(d)(4) of this section;

(d)(5)(iii)-If a mixture has not been tested as a whole to determine whether the mixture is a physical hazard, the chemical manufacturer, importer, or employer may use whatever scientifically valid data is available to evaluate the physical hazard potential of the mixture; and,

transport definitions, test methods and classification criteria were used as a basis for the work since they were already substantially harmonized. The work proceeded through examination of the scientific basis for the criteria, gaining consensus on the test methods, data interpretation and on the criteria. For most hazard classes, the existing schemes were already in place and being used by the transport sector. On this basis, a portion of the work focused on ensuring that workplace, environment and consumer safety issues were adequately addressed.

LABELS
Comparison -The NEW GHS label requirements are very specific. GHS labels now have pictograms, as well as specific signal words, and hazard statements. See the pictogram table and label element comparison. With the addition of the use of transport pictograms in non-transport settings. The NEW GHS Label requirements have changed dramatically with the addition of Pictograms for labeling Hazardous Chemicals. Study them carefully and make sure all employees are Trained to know them!

OLD –HCS- 29 CFR 1910.1200	NEW –GHS - The Globally Harmonized System for Hazard Communication.
(f) Labels and Other Forms of Warning	**Application of standardization in the harmonized system.**
(f)(1)-The chemical manufacturer, importer, or distributor shall ensure that each container of hazardous chemicals leaving the workplace is labeled, tagged or marked with the following information:	For labels, the hazard symbols, signal words and hazard statements have all been standardized and assigned to each of the hazard categories. These standardized elements should not be subject to variation, and should appear on the GHS labels as indicated.
(f)(1) (i)-Identity of the hazardous chemical(s);	**Use of non-standardized or supplemental information**
(f)(1)(ii) -Appropriate hazard warnings; and	There are many other label elements which may appear on a label which have not been standardized in the harmonized system. Some of these clearly need to be included on the label, for example precautionary statements. Competent authorities may require additional information, or suppliers may choose to add supplementary information on their own initiative. In order to ensure that the use of non-standardized information
(f)(1)(iii)-Name and address of the chemical manufacturer, importer, or other responsible party.	
(f)(4)-If the hazardous chemical is regulated by OSHA in a substance-specific health	

standard, the chemical manufacturer, importer, distributor or employer shall ensure that the labels or other forms of warning used are in accordance with the requirements of that standard.

(f)(6)-The employer may use signs, placards, process sheets, batch tickets, operating procedures, or other such written materials in lieu of affixing labels to individual stationary process containers, as long as the alternative method identifies the containers to which it is applicable and conveys the information required by paragraph (f)(5) of this section to be on a label. The written materials shall be readily accessible to the employees in their work area throughout each work shift.

(f)(7)-The employer is not required to label portable containers into which hazardous chemicals are transferred from labeled containers, and which are intended only for the immediate use of the employee who performs the transfer. For purposes of this section, drugs which are dispensed by a pharmacy to a health care provider for direct administration to a patient are

does not lead to unnecessarily wide variation in information or undermine GHS information, the use of supplementary information should be limited to the following circumstances:

(a) The supplementary information provides further detail and does not contradict or cast doubt on the validity of the standardized hazard information; or;

(b) The supplementary information provides information about hazards not yet incorporated into the GHS.

In either instance, the supplementary information should not lower standards of protection.

The labeler should have the option of providing supplementary information related to the hazard, such as physical state or route of exposure, with the hazard statement rather than in the supplementary information section on the label.

Labeling Procedures :

The following sections describe the procedures for preparing labels in the GHS, comprising the following:
(a) Allocation of label elements;
(b) Reproduction of the symbol;
(c) Reproduction of the hazard pictogram;
(d) Signal words;
(e) Hazard statements;
(f) Precautionary statements and pictograms;

exempted from labeling.

(f)(11)-Chemical manufacturers, importers, distributors, or employers who become newly aware of any significant information regarding the hazards of a chemical shall revise the labels for the chemical within three months of becoming aware of the new information. Labels on containers of hazardous chemicals shipped after that time shall contain the new information. If the chemical is not currently produced or imported, the chemical manufacturer, importers, distributor, or employer shall add the information to the label before The chemical is shipped or introduced into the workplace again.

(g) Product and supplier identification;

(h) Multiple hazards and precedence of information;

(i) Arrangements for presenting the GHS label elements; and

(j) Special Labeling arrangements.

Label Elements:
The tables in the individual Chapters for each hazard class detail the label elements (symbol, signal word, hazard statement) that have been assigned to each of the hazard categories of the GHS. Hazard categories reflect the harmonized classification criteria. A summary of the allocation of label elements is provided below. There are special arrangements, which apply to the use of certain mixture concentrations in the GHS to take account of the information needs of different target audiences.

Information required on a GHS label:

(a) Signal words -A signal word means a word used to indicate the relative level of severity of hazard and alert the reader to a potential hazard on the label. The signal words used in the GHS are "Danger" and "Warning". "Danger" is used for the more severe hazard categories (i.e. in the main for hazard categories 1 and 2), while "Warning" is used for the less severe. The tables in the individual Chapters for each hazard class detail the signal words that have been assigned to each of the hazard categories of the GHS.

(b) Hazard statements -A hazard statement means a phrase assigned to a hazard class and category that describes the nature of the hazards of a hazardous product, including, where appropriate, the degree of hazard. The tables of label elements in the individual Chapters for each hazard class detail the hazard statements that have been assigned to each of the hazard categories of the GHS.

(c) Pictograms -A pictogram means a graphical composition that includes a symbol plus other graphic elements, such as a border, background pattern or color that is intended to convey specific information. There are 9 symbols used in the pictograms: flame, flame over circle, exploding bomb, corrosion, gas cylinder, skull and crossbones, exclamation point, environment, and health hazard.

All hazard pictograms used in the GHS should be in the shape of a square set at a point.

Pictograms prescribed by the GHS but not the UN Recommendations on the Transport of Dangerous Goods, Model Regulations, should have a black symbol on a white background with a red frame sufficiently wide to be clearly visible. However, when such a pictogram appears on a label for a package which will not be exported, the Competent Authority may choose to give suppliers and employers discretion to use a black border. Competent Authorities may allow

	The use of UN Recommendations on the Transport of Dangerous Goods. Pictograms prescribed by the UN Recommendations on the Transport of Dangerous Goods, Model Regulations will use a background and symbol color as specified by those regulations.
	(d) Precautionary Statements -A precautionary statement means a phrase (and/or pictogram) that describes recommended measures that should be taken to minimize or prevent adverse effects resulting from exposure to a hazardous product, or improper storage or handling of a hazardous product. The GHS label should include appropriate precautionary information, the choice of which is with the labeler or the competent authority.
	Product Identifier:
	(i) A product identifier should be used on a GHS label and it should match the product identifier used on the SDS. Where a substance or mixture is covered by the UN Model Regulations on the Transport of Dangerous Goods, the UN proper shipping name should also be used on the package;

	(ii) The label for a substance should include the chemical identity of the substance. For mixtures or alloys, the label should include the chemical identities of all ingredients or alloying elements that contribute to acute toxicity, skin corrosion or serious eye damage, germ cell mutagenicity, carcinogenicity, reproductive toxicity, skin or respiratory sensitization, or Target Organ Systemic Toxicity (TOST), when these hazards appear on the label. Alternatively, the Competent Authority may require the inclusion of all ingredients or alloying elements that contribute to the hazard of the mixture or alloy;
	(iii) Where a substance or mixture is supplied exclusively for workplace use, the Competent authority may choose to give suppliers discretion to include chemical identities on the SDS, in lieu of including them on labels;
	(iv) The competent authority rules for CBI take priority over the rules for product identification. This means that where an ingredient would normally be included on the label, if it meets the competent authority criteria for CBI, its identity does not have to be included on the label.

	(e) Supplier Identification:
	Location of GHS information on the label The GHS hazard pictograms, signal word and hazard statements should be located together on the label. The Competent Authority may choose to provide a specified layout for the presentation of these and for the presentation of precautionary information, or allow supplier discretion.

WORKPLACE LABELING
Comparison -The **OLD** HCS Workplace Labeling is allowed in the NEW GHS. This is a common practice in many USA Workplaces.

OLD - HCS -29 CFR 1910.1200	NEW –GHS - The Globally Harmonized System for Hazard Communication.
(f) (6)-(7) Workplace Labeling **(f)(6)**-The employer may use signs, placards, process sheets, batch tickets, operating procedures, or other such written materials in lieu of affixing labels to individual stationary process containers, as long as the alternative method identifies the containers to which it is applicable and conveys the information required by	**Workplace Labeling** Products falling within the scope of the GHS will carry the GHS label at the point where they are supplied to the workplace, and that label should be maintained on the supplied container in the workplace. The GHS label or label elements should also be used for workplace containers. However, the competent authority can allow employers to use alternative means of giving workers the same information in a different written or displayed format when such a format is more appropriate to the workplace and communicates the

paragraph (f)(5) of this section to be on a label. The written materials shall be readily accessible to the employees in their work area throughout each work shift.

(f)(7)-The employer is not required to label portable containers into which hazardous chemicals are transferred from labeled containers, and which are intended only for the immediate use of the employee who performs the transfer. For purposes of this section, drugs which are dispensed by a pharmacy to a health care provider for direct administration to a patient are exempted from labeling.

information as effectively as the GHS label. For example, label information could be displayed in the work area, rather than on the individual containers.

Alternative means of providing workers with the information contained in GHS labels are needed usually where hazardous chemicals are transferred from an original supplier container into a workplace container or system, or where chemicals are produced in a workplace but are not packaged in containers intended for sale or supply. Chemicals that are produced in a workplace may be contained or stored in many different ways such as: small samples collected for testing or analysis, piping systems including valves, process or reaction vessels, ore cars, conveyer systems or free-standing bulk storage of solids. In batch manufacturing processes, one mixing vessel may be used to contain a number of different chemical mixtures.

In many situations, it is impractical to produce a complete GHS label and attach it to the container, due, for example, to container size limitations or lack of access to a process container. Some examples of workplace situations where chemicals may be transferred from supplier containers include: containers for laboratory testing or analysis, storage vessels, piping or process reaction systems or temporary containers where the chemical will be used by one worker within a short time frame. Decanted chemicals intended for immediate use could be labeled with the main components and directly refer the

| | user to the supplier label information and SDS.

All such systems should ensure that there is clear hazard communication. Workers should be trained to understand the specific communication methods used in a workplace. Examples of alternative methods include: use of product identifiers together with GHS symbols and other pictograms to describe precautionary measures; use of process flow charts for complex systems to identify chemicals contained in pipes and vessels with links to the appropriate SDS; use of displays with GHS symbols, color and signal words in piping systems and processing equipment; use of permanent placarding for fixed piping; use of batch tickets or recipes for labeling batch mixing vessels and use of piping bands with hazard symbols and product identifiers. |

UPDATING LABELS

Comparison -The **OLD** HCS requirements for Updating Labels are the same in the NEW GHS.

OLD –HCS- 29 CFR 1910.1200	NEW –GHS - The Globally Harmonized System for Hazard Communication.
(f)(11) Updating Labels	**Updating Labels**
(f)(11)-Chemical manufacturers, importers, distributors, or employers who become newly aware of any significant information regarding the hazards of a chemical shall revise the labels for the chemical within three months of becoming aware of the new information. Labels on containers of hazardous chemicals shipped after that time shall contain the new information. If the chemical is not currently produced or imported, the chemical manufacturer, importers, distributor, or employer shall add the information to the label before the chemical is shipped or introduced into the workplace again.	All systems should specify a means of responding in an appropriate and timely manner to new information and updating labels and SDS information accordingly. The following are examples of how this could be achieved. Suppliers should respond to "new and significant" information they receive about a chemical hazard by updating the label and safety data sheet for that chemical. New and significant information is any information that changes the GHS classification of the substance or mixture and leads to a resulting change in the information provided on the label or any information concerning the chemical and appropriate control measures that may affect the SDS. This could include, for example, new information on the potential adverse chronic health effects of exposure as a result of recently published documentation or test results, even if a change in classification may not yet be triggered. Updating should be carried out promptly on receipt of the information that necessitates the revision. The competent

	authority may choose to specify a time limit within which the information should be revised. This applies only to labels and SDS for products that are not subject to an approval mechanism such as pesticides. In pesticide labeling systems, where the label is part of the product approval mechanism, suppliers cannot update the supply label on their own initiative. However when the products are subject to the transport of dangerous goods requirements, the label used should be updated on receipt of the new information, as above. Suppliers should also periodically review the information on which the label and safety data sheet for a substance or mixture is based, even if no new and significant information has been provided to them in respect of that substance or mixture. This will require e.g. a search of chemical hazard databases for new information. The competent authority may choose to specify a time (typically 3 -- 5 years) from the date of original preparation, within which suppliers should review the labels and SDS information.

MSDS/SDS SHEETS	
Comparison -The OLD Performance Orientation of the HCS MSDS will be changed. The NEW GHS requires a 16 section MSDS format with a specific sequence and minimum required contents. See the table below for more detailed comparisons of MSDS sections/information.	
OLD –HCS- 29 CFR1910.1200	**NEW – GHS- The Globally Harmonized System for Hazard Communication.**
(g) MSDS	**Minimum information for an SDS**
(g)(2)-Each material safety data sheet shall be in English (although the employer may maintain copies in other languages as well), and shall contain at least the following information:	**(1)** Product and company identification - GHS product identifier - Other means of identification. - Recommended use of the chemical and restrictions on use. - Supplier's details (including name, address, phone number etc). - Emergency phone number
(g)(2)(i)-The identity used on the label, and, except as provided for in paragraph (i) of this section on trade secrets:	**(2) Hazards identification** - GHS classification of the substance/mixture and any regional information.
(g)(2)(i)(A)-If the hazardous chemical is a single substance, its chemical and common name(s);	- GHS label elements, including precautionary statements. (Hazard symbols may be provided as a graphical reproduction of the symbols in black and white or the name of the symbol e.g. flame, skull and crossbones.)
(g)(2)(i)(B)-If the hazardous chemical is a mixture which has been tested as a whole to determine its hazards, the chemical and common name(s) of the ingredients which contribute to these known hazards, and the common name(s) of the	- Other hazards which do not result in classification (e.g. dust explosion hazard) or are not covered by the GHS.

mixture itself; or, **(g)(2)(i)(C)**-If the hazardous chemical is a mixture which has not been tested as a whole: **(g)(2)(i)(C)(1)**-The chemical and common name(s) of all ingredients which have been determined to be health hazards, and which comprise 1% or greater of the composition, except that chemicals identified as carcinogens under paragraph (d) of this section shall be listed if the concentrations are 0.1% or greater; and, **(g)(2)(i)(C)(2)**-The chemical and common name(s) of all ingredients which have been determined to be health hazards, and which comprise less than 1% (0.1% for carcinogens) of the mixture, if there is evidence that the ingredient(s) could be released from the mixture in concentrations which would exceed an established OSHA permissible exposure limit or ACGIH Threshold Limit Value, or could present a health risk to employees; and, **(g)(2)(i)(C)(3)**-The chemical	**(3)Composition/ Information On Ingredients Substance** - Chemical identity - Common name, synonyms etc. - CAS number, EC number etc. - Impurities and stabilizing additives which are themselves classified and which contribute to the classification of the substance. Mixture - The chemical identity and concentration or concentration ranges of all ingredients which are hazardous within the meaning of the GHS and are present above their cut-off levels. - Cutoff level for reproductive toxicity, carcinogenicity and category 1 mutagenicity is $\geq 0.1\%$ - Cutoff level for all other hazard classes is $\geq 1\%$ For information on ingredients, the competent authority rules for CBI take priority over the rules for product identification. **(4) First-aid measures** - Description of necessary measures, subdivided according to the different routes of exposure, i.e. inhalation, skin and eye contact and ingestion. - Most important symptoms/effects, acute and delayed. - Indication of immediate medical attention and special treatment needed, if necessary **(5) Fire-fighting measures** Suitable (and unsuitable) extinguishing media. Specific hazards arising from the

and common name(s) of all ingredients which have been determined to present a physical hazard when present in the mixture;

(g)(2)(ii)-Physical and chemical characteristics of the hazardous chemical (such as vapor pressure, flash point);

(g)(2)(iii)-The physical hazards of the hazardous chemical, including the potential for fire, explosion, and reactivity;

(g)(2)(iv)-The health hazards of the hazardous chemical, including signs and symptoms of exposure, and any medical conditions which are generally recognized as being aggravated by exposure to the chemical;

(g)(2)(v)-The primary route(s) of entry;

(g)(2)(vi)
The OSHA permissible exposure limit, ACGIH Threshold Limit Value, and any other exposure limit used or recommended by the chemical manufacturer, importer, or employer preparing the material safety data sheet, where available;

chemical (e.g. nature of any hazardous combustion products).
- Special protective equipment and precautions for fire-fighters

(6) Accidental release measures
- Personal precautions, protective equipment and emergency procedures.
- Environmental precautions.
- Methods and materials for containment and cleaning up.

(7) Handling and storage
- Precautions for safe handling.
- Conditions for safe storage, including any incompatibilities

(8) Exposure controls/personal protection
- Control parameters e.g. occupational exposure limit values or biological limit values.
- Appropriate engineering controls.
- Individual protection measures, such as personal protective equipment

(9)Physical and chemical properties
- Appearance (physical state, color etc)
- Odor
- Odor threshold
- pH
- melting point/freezing point
- initial boiling point and boiling range
- flash point:
- evaporation rate
- flammability (solid, gas)
- upper/lower flammability or explosive limits
- vapor pressure
- vapor density

(g)(2)(vii)-Whether the hazardous chemical is listed in the National Toxicology Program (NTP) Annual Report on Carcinogens (latest edition) or has been found to be a potential carcinogen in the International Agency for Research on Cancer (IARC) Monographs (latest editions), or by OSHA;	- relative density: - solubility(ies) - partition coefficient: n-octanol/water: - auto-ignition temperature decomposition temperature **(10) Stability and reactivity- Chemical stability.** - Possibility of hazardous reactions. - Conditions to avoid (e.g. static discharge, shock or vibration) - Incompatible materials - Hazardous decomposition products
(g)(2)(viii)-Any generally applicable precautions for safe handling and use which are known to the chemical manufacturer, importer or employer preparing the material safety data sheet, including appropriate hygienic practices, protective measures during repair and maintenance of contaminated equipment, and procedures for clean-up of spills and leaks; **(g)(2)(ix)**-Any generally applicable control measures which are known to the chemical manufacturer, importer or employer preparing the material safety data sheet, such as appropriate engineering controls, work practices, or personal protective equipment;	**(11) Toxicological information** Concise but complete and comprehensible description of the various toxicological (health) effects and the available data used to identify those effects, including: - information on the likely routes of exposure (inhalation, ingestion, skin and eye contact); - Symptoms related to the physical, chemical and toxicological characteristics; - Delayed and immediate effects and also chronic effects from short- and long-term exposure. - Numerical measures of toxicity (such as acute toxicity estimates). **(12) Ecological information** - Ecotoxicity (aquatic and terrestrial, where available). - Persistence and degradability - Bioaccumulative potential - Mobility in soil - Other adverse effects **(13) Disposal considerations** - Description of waste residues and information on their safe handling and methods of disposal, including any contaminated packaging.

(g)(2)(x)-Emergency and first aid procedures;	**(14) Transport information**
	- UN number
(g)(2)(xi)-The date of preparation of the material safety data sheet or the last change to it; and,	- UN Proper shipping name.
	- Transport Hazard class(es).
	- Packing group, if applicable.
	- Marine pollutant (Yes/No).
	- Special precautions which a user needs to be aware of or needs to comply with in connection with transport or conveyance either within or outside their premises.
(g)(2)(xii)-The name, address and telephone number of the chemical manufacturer, importer, employer or other responsible party preparing or distributing the material safety data sheet, who can provide additional information on the hazardous chemical and appropriate emergency procedures, if necessary.	
	(15) Regulatory information
	- Safety, health and environmental regulations specific for the product in question.
	(16) Other information
	- Other information including information on preparation and revision of the SDS
(g)(3)-If no relevant information is found for any given category on the material safety data sheet, the chemical manufacturer, importer or employer preparing the material safety data sheet shall mark it to indicate that no applicable information was found.	**Criteria for determining whether an SDS should be produced.**
	An SDS should be produced for all substances and mixtures which meet the harmonized criteria for physical, health or environmental hazards under the GHS and for all mixtures which contain substances that meet the criteria for carcinogenic, toxic to reproduction or target organ systemic toxicity in concentrations exceeding the cut-off limits for SDS specified by the criteria for mixtures .The competent authority may choose also to require SDSs for mixtures not meeting the criteria for classification as hazardous but which contain hazardous substances in certain concentrations.
(g)(5) [MSDS Updating: The chemical manufacturer, importer or employer preparing the material safety data sheet shall ensure that the information recorded	

accurately reflects the scientific evidence used in making the hazard determination. If the chemical manufacturer, importer or employer preparing the material safety data sheet becomes newly aware of any significant information regarding the hazards of a chemical, or ways to protect against the hazards, this new information shall be added to the material safety data sheet within three months. If the chemical is not currently being produced or imported the chemical manufacturer or importer Shall add the information to the material safety data sheet before the chemical is introduced into the workplace again.

(g)(10) MSDS Format :

Material safety data sheets may be kept in any form, including operating procedures, and may be designed to cover groups of hazardous chemicals in a work area where it may be more appropriate to address the hazards of a process rather than individual hazardous chemicals. However, the employer shall

An SDS should be provided based on the following generic cut-off /concentration limits:

≥ 1% for acute toxicity, skin corrosion/irritation, serious damage to eyes/eye irritation, respiratory/skin sensitization, mutagenicity category 2, target organ toxicity (single & repeat) exposures, and hazardous to the environment; and

≥ 0.1% for mutagenicity category 1, carcinogenicity and reproductive toxicity.

Classification of Hazardous Substances and Mixtures

There may be some cases when the available hazard data may justify classification on the basis of other cut-off-limits than the generic ones specified in the health and environment hazard class. When such specific cut-offs are used for classification, they should also apply to the obligation to compile an SDS.

Some competent authorities (CA) may require SDSs to be compiled for mixtures which are not classified for acute toxicity or aquatic toxicity as a result of application of the additivity formula, but which contain acutely toxic substances or substances toxic to the aquatic environment in concentrations equal to or greater than 1 %.

ensure that in all cases the required information is provided for each hazardous chemical, and is readily accessible during each work shift to employees when they are in their work area(s).	In accordance with the building block principle, some competent authorities may choose not to regulate certain categories within a hazard class. In such situations, there would be no obligation to compile a SDS.

UPDATING MSDS/SDS SHEETS	
Comparison -The OLD HCS requirements for updating MSDS Sheets are the same in the NEW GHS.	
OLD –HCS – 29 CFR 1910.1200	**NEW –GHS- The Globally Harmonized System for Hazard Communication.**
(g)(5) Updating MSDS Sheets The chemical manufacturer, importer or employer preparing the material safety data sheet shall ensure that the information recorded accurately reflects the scientific evidence used in making the hazard determination. If the chemical manufacturer, importer or employer preparing the material safety data sheet becomes newly aware of any significant information regarding the hazards of a chemical, or ways to protect against the hazards, this new information shall be added to the material safety data sheet within three months. If the chemical is not currently being produced or imported the chemical manufacturer or importer shall add the information to the material safety data sheet before the chemical is introduced into the workplace again.	**Updating SDS Sheets** All systems should specify a means of responding in an appropriate and timely manner to new information and updating labels and SDS information accordingly. The following are examples of how this could be achieved. Suppliers should respond to "new and significant" information they receive about a chemical hazard by updating the label and safety data sheet for that chemical. New and significant information is any information that changes the GHS classification of the substance or mixture and leads to a resulting change in the information provided on the label or any information concerning the chemical and appropriate control measures that may affect the SDS. This could include, for example, new information on the potential adverse chronic health effects of exposure as a result of recently published documentation or test results, even if a change in classification may not yet be triggered.

	Updating should be carried out promptly on receipt of the information that necessitates the revision. The competent authority may choose to specify a time limit within which the information should be revised. This applies only to labels and SDS for products that are not subject to an approval mechanism such as pesticides. In pesticide labeling systems, where the label is part of the product approval mechanism, suppliers cannot update the supply label on their own initiative. However when the products are subject to the transport of dangerous goods requirements, the label used should be updated on receipt of the new information, as above. Suppliers should also periodically review the information on which the label and safety data sheet for a substance or mixture is based, even if no new and significant information has been provided to them in respect of that substance or mixture. This will require e.g. a search of chemical hazard databases for new information. The competent authority may choose to specify a time (typically 3 -- 5 years) from the date of original preparation, within which suppliers should review the labels and SDS information.

INFORMATION & TRAINING

Comparison -The NEW GHS has broad general training requirements. The OLD HCS has more detailed training requirements than the GHS.

OLD –HCS – 29 CFR 1910.1200	NEW –GHS - The Globally Harmonized System for Hazard Communication.
(h) "Employee information and training." **(h)(1)**-Employers shall provide employees with effective information and training on hazardous chemicals in their work area at the time of their initial assignment, and whenever a new physical or health hazard the employees have not previously been trained about is introduced into their work area. Information and training may be designed to cover categories of hazards (e.g., flammability, carcinogenicity) or specific chemicals. Chemical-specific information must always be available through labels and material safety data sheets. **(h)(2)**-"Information." Employees shall be informed of: **(h)(2)(i)**-The requirements of this section; **(h)(2)(ii)**-Any operations in their work area where hazardous chemicals are present; and,	Training users of hazard information is an integral part of hazard communication. Systems should identify the appropriate education and training for GHS target audiences who are required to interpret label and/or SDS information and to take appropriate action in response to chemical hazards. Training requirements should be appropriate for and commensurate with the nature of the work or exposure. Key target audiences for training include workers, emergency responders, and those involved in the preparation of labels, SDS and hazard communication strategies as part of risk management systems. Others involved in the transport and supply of hazardous chemicals also require training to varying degrees. In addition, systems should consider strategies required for educating consumers in interpreting label information on products that they use.

(h)(2)(iii)-The location and availability of the written hazard communication program, including the required list(s) of hazardous chemicals, and material safety data sheets required by this section.

(h)(3)-"Training." Employee training shall include at least:

(h)(3)(i)-Methods and observations that may be used to detect the presence or release of a hazardous chemical in the work area (such as monitoring conducted by the employer, continuous monitoring devices, visual appearance or odor of hazardous chemicals when being released, etc.);

(h)(3)(ii)-The physical and health hazards of the chemicals in the work area;

(h)(3)(iii)-The measures employees can take to protect themselves from these hazards, including specific procedures the employer has implemented to protect employees from exposure to hazardous chemicals, such as appropriate work practices, emergency procedures, and personal protective equipment to be used; and,

(h)(3)(iv)-The details of the hazard communication program developed by the employer, including an explanation of the labeling system and the material safety data sheet,

and how employees can obtain and use the appropriate hazard information.	

TRADE SECRETS /CBI	
Comparison -The NEW GHS provides many of the same CBI principles. The HCS is the same with the CBI principles in the GHS.	
OLD –HCS- 29 CFR 1910.1200	**NEW –GHS - The Globally Harmonized System for Hazard Communication.**
i) "Trade secrets."	**Confidential Business information**
(i)(1)- Chemical name and other specific identification of a hazardous chemical, from the material safety data sheet, provided that: **(i)(1)(i)**-The claim that the information withheld is a trade secret can be supported; **(i)(1)(ii)**-Information contained in the material safety data sheet concerning the properties and effects of the hazardous chemical is disclosed; **(i)(1)(iii)**-The material safety data sheet indicates that the specific chemical identity is being withheld as a trade secret; and, **(i)(1)(iv)**-The specific chemical identity is made available to health professionals, employees, and designated representatives in accordance with the applicable provisions of this paragraph.	Systems adopting the GHS should consider what provisions may be appropriate for the protection of confidential business information (CBI). Such provisions should not compromise the health and safety of workers or consumers, or the protection of the environment. As with other parts of the GHS, the rules of the importing country should apply with respect to CBI claims for imported substances and mixtures. Where a system chooses to provide for protection of confidential business information, competent authorities should establish appropriate mechanisms, in accordance with national law and practice, and consider: **(a)** Whether the inclusion of certain chemicals or classes of chemicals in the arrangements is appropriate to the needs of the system; (b) what definition of "confidential business information" should apply, taking account of factors such as the accessibility of the information by

(i)(2)-Where a treating physician or nurse determines that a medical emergency exists and the specific chemical identity of a hazardous chemical is necessary for emergency or first-aid treatment, the chemical manufacturer, importer, or employer shall immediately disclose the specific chemical identity of a trade secret chemical to that treating physician or nurse, regardless of the existence of a written statement of need or a confidentiality agreement. The chemical manufacturer, importer, or employer may require a written statement of need and confidentiality agreement, In accordance with the provisions of paragraphs (i)(3) and (4) of this section, as soon as circumstances permit.

(i)(3)-In non-emergency situations, a chemical manufacturer, importer, or employer shall, upon request, disclose a specific chemical identity, otherwise permitted to be withheld under paragraph (i)(1) of this section, to a health professional (i.e. physician, industrial hygienist, toxicologist, epidemiologist, or occupational health nurse) providing medical or other occupational health services to exposed employee(s), and to employees or designated representatives, if:

competitors, intellectual property rights and the potential harm disclosure would cause to the employer or supplier's business; and

(c) Appropriate procedures for the disclosure of confidential business information, where necessary to protect the health and safety of workers or consumers, or to protect the environment, and measures to prevent further disclosure. Specific provisions for the protection of confidential business information may differ among systems In accordance with national law and practice. However, they should be consistent with the following general principles:

(a) For information otherwise required on labels or safety data sheets, CBI claims should be limited to the names of chemicals, and their concentrations in mixtures. All other information should be disclosed on the label and/or safety data sheet, as required;

(b) Where CBI has been withheld, the label or chemical safety data sheet should so indicate;

(c) CBI should be disclosed to the competent authority upon request. The competent authority should protect the confidentiality of the information In accordance with applicable law and practice;

(i)(3)(i)-The request is in writing;

(i)(3)(ii)-The request describes with reasonable detail one or more of the following occupational health needs for the information:

(i)(3)(ii)(A)-To assess the hazards of the chemicals to which employees will be exposed;

(i)(3)(ii)(B)-To conduct or assess sampling of the workplace atmosphere to determine employee exposure levels;

i)(3)(ii)(C)-To conduct pre-assignment or periodic medical surveillance of exposed employees;

(i)(3)(ii)(D)-To provide medical treatment to exposed employees;

(i)(3)(ii)(E)-To select or assess appropriate personal protective equipment for exposed employees;

(i)(3)(ii)(F)-To design or assess engineering controls or other protective measures for exposed employees; and,

(i)(3)(ii)(G)-To conduct studies to determine the health effects of exposure

(d) Where a medical professional determines that a medical emergency exists due to exposure to a hazardous chemical or a chemical mixture, mechanisms should be in place to ensure timely disclosure by the supplier or employer or competent authority of any specific confidential information necessary for treatment. The medical professional should maintain the confidentiality of the information;

(e) For non-emergency situations, the supplier or employer should ensure disclosure of confidential information to a safety or health professional providing medical or other safety and health services to exposed workers or consumers, and to workers or workers' representatives. Persons requesting the information should provide specific reasons for the disclosure, and should agree to use the information only for the purpose of consumer or worker protection, and to otherwise maintain its confidentiality;

(f) Where non-disclosure of CBI is challenged, the competent authority should address such challenges or provide for an alternative process for challenges. The supplier or employer should be responsible for supporting the assertion that the withheld information qualifies for CBI protection.

(i)(3)(iii)-The request explains in detail why the disclosure of the specific chemical identity is essential and that, in lieu thereof, the disclosure of the following information to the health professional, employee, or designated representative, would not satisfy the purposes described in paragraph (i)(3)(ii) of this section:

(i)(3)(iii)(A)-The properties and effects of the chemical;

(i)(3)(iii)(B)-Measures for controlling workers' exposure to the chemical;

(i)(3)(iii)(C)-Methods of monitoring and analyzing worker exposure to the chemical; and,

(i)(3)(iii)(D)-Methods of diagnosing and treating harmful exposures to the chemical;

(i)(3)(iv) -The request includes a description of the procedures to be used to maintain the confidentiality of the disclosed information; and,

(i)(3)(v) -The health professional, and the employer or contractor of the services of the health professional (i.e. downstream employer, labor organization, or individual employee), employee, or designated representative, agree in a written confidentiality agreement that the health professional, employee, or designated representative, will not use the trade secret information for any purpose other than the health need(s) asserted and agree not to release the information under any circumstances other than to OSHA, as provided in paragraph (i)(6) of this section, except as authorized by the terms of the agreement or by the chemical manufacturer, importer, or employer

(i)(4)-The confidentiality agreement authorized by paragraph(i)(3)(iv) of this section:

(i)(4)(i)-May restrict the use of the information to the health purposes indicated in the written statement of need;

(i)(4)(ii)-May provide for appropriate legal remedies in the event of a breach of the agreement, including stipulation of a reasonable pre-estimate of likely damages; and,

(i)(4)(iii)-May not include requirements for the posting of a penalty bond.

(i)(5)-Nothing in this standard is meant to preclude the parties from pursuing non-contractual remedies to the extent permitted by law.

(i)(6)-If the health professional, employee, or designated representative receiving the trade secret information decides that there is a need to disclose it to OSHA, the chemical manufacturer, importer, or employer who provided the limitations or conditions upon the disclosure of the requested chemical information as may be appropriate to assure that the occupational health services are provided without an undue risk of harm to the chemical manufacturer, importer, or employer.

(i)(11)-If a citation for a failure to release specific chemical identity information is contested by the chemical manufacturer, importer, or employer, the matter will be adjudicated before the Occupational Safety and Health Review Commission in accordance with the Act's enforcement scheme and the applicable Commission rules of procedure. In accordance with the Commission rules, when a chemical manufacturer, importer, or employer continues to withhold the information during the contest, the Administrative Law Judge may review the citation and supporting documentation "in camera" or issue appropriate orders to protect the confidentiality of such matters.

(i)(12)-Notwithstanding the existence of a trade secret claim, a chemical manufacturer, importer, or employer shall, upon request, disclose to the Assistant Secretary any information which this section requires the chemical manufacturer, importer, or employer to make available. Where there is a trade secret claim, such claim shall be made no later than at the time the information is provided to the Assistant Secretary so that suitable determinations of trade secret status can be made and the necessary protections can be implemented.

(i)(13)-Nothing in this paragraph shall be construed as requiring the disclosure under any circumstances of process or percentage of mixture information which is a trade secret.

Appendix D Definition of Trade Secret (Mandatory)

The following is a reprint of the "Restatement of Torts"

b. "Definition of trade secret." A trade secret may consist of any formula, pattern, device or compilation of information which is used in one's business, and which gives him an opportunity to obtain an advantage over competitors who do not know or use it. It may be a formula for a chemical compound, a process of manufacturing, treating or preserving materials, a pattern for a machine or other device, or a list of customers. It differs from other secret information in a business (see s759 of the Restatement of Torts which is not included in this Appendix) in that it is not simply information as to single or ephemeral events in the conduct of the business, as, for example, the amount or other terms of a secret bid for a contract or the salary of certain employees, or the security investments made or contemplated, or the date fixed for the announcement of a new policy or for bringing out a new model or the like. A trade secret is a process or device for continuous use in the operations of the business. Generally it relates to the production of goods, as, for example, a machine or formula for the production of an article. It may, however, relate to the sale of goods or to other operations in the business, such as a code for determining discounts, rebates or other concessions in a price list or catalog, or a list of specialized customers, or a method of bookkeeping or other office management.

"Secrecy." The subject matter of a trade secret must be secret. Matters of public knowledge or of general knowledge in an industry cannot be appropriated by one as his secret. Matters which are completely disclosed by the goods which one markets cannot be his secret. Substantially, a trade secret is known only in the particular business in which it is used. It is not requisite that only the proprietor of the business know it. He may, without losing his protection, communicate it to employees involved in its use. He may likewise communicate it to others pledged to secrecy. Others may also know of it independently, as, for example, when they have discovered the process or formula by independent invention and are keeping it secret. Nevertheless, a substantial element of secrecy must exist, so that, except by the use of improper means, there would be difficulty in acquiring the information. An exact definition of a trade secret is not possible. Some factors to be considered in determining whether given information is one's trade secret are: (1) The extent to which the information is known outside of his business; (2) the extent to which it is known by employees and others involved in his business; (3) the extent of measures taken by him to guard the secrecy of the information; (4) the value of the information to him and his competitors; (5) the amount of effort or money expended by him in developing the information; (6) the ease or difficulty with which the information could be properly acquired or duplicated by others.

"Novelty and prior art." A trade secret may be a device or process which is patentable; but it need not be that. It may be a device or process which is clearly anticipated in the prior art or one which is merely a mechanical improvement that a good mechanic can make. Novelty and invention are not requisite for a trade secret as they are for patentability. These requirements are essential to patentability because a patent protects against unlicensed use of the patented device or process even by one who discovers it properly through independent research. The patent monopoly is a reward to the inventor. But such is not the case with a trade secret. Its protection is not based on a policy of rewarding or otherwise encouraging the development of secret processes or devices. The protection is merely against breach of faith and reprehensible means of learning another's secret. For this limited protection it is not appropriate to require also the kind of novelty and invention which is a requisite of patentability. The nature of the secret is, however, an important factor in determining the kind of relief that is appropriate against one who is subject to liability under the rule stated in this section Thus, if the secret consists of a device or process which is a novel invention, one who acquires

the secret wrongfully is ordinarily enjoined from further use of it and is required to account for the profits derived from his past use. If, on the other hand, the secret consists of mechanical improvements that a good mechanic can make without resort to the secret, the wrongdoer's liability may be limited to damages, and an injunction against future use of the improvements made with the aid of the secret may be inappropriate.	

MULTIPLE HAZARDS/PRECEDENCE

Comparison-The NEW GHS requires strict Label requirements for multiple hazards with prescribed pictograms and statements.

OLD-HCS -29 CFR 1910.1200	**NEW –GHS- The Globally Harmonized System for Hazard Communication.**
Multiple Hazards Appendix A - The label is intended to be an immediate visual reminder of the hazards of a chemical. It is not necessary, however, that every hazard presented by a chemical be listed on the label. Manufacturers, importers, and distributors will have to assess the evidence regarding the product's hazards and must consider exposures under	**Multiple Hazards and precedence of Hazard Information:** The following arrangements apply where a substance or mixture presents more than one GHS hazard. Therefore where a system does not provide information on the label for a particular hazard, the application of the arrangements should be modified accordingly. **Precedence for the Allocation of Symbols**: For substances and mixtures covered by the UN Recommendations on the Transport

normal circumstances of use or foreseeable emergencies when evaluating what hazards to put on the label. This is not to say that only acute hazards are to be listed on the label, or that well-substantiated hazards should be left off the label because they appear on the data sheet.

of Dangerous Goods, Model Regulations, the precedence of symbols for physical hazards should follow the rules of the UN Model Regulations. In workplace situations, the Competent Authority may require all symbols for physical hazards to be used. For health hazards the following principles of precedence apply:

(a) If the skull and crossbones applies, the exclamation mark should not appear;

(b) If the corrosive symbol applies, the exclamation mark should not appear where it is used for skin or eye irritation;

(c) If the new health hazard symbol appears for respiratory sensitization, the exclamation mark should not appear where it is used for skin sensitization or for skin or eye irritation.

Precedence for allocation of signal words If the signal word 'Danger' applies, the signal word 'Warning' should not appear.

Precedence for allocation of Hazard Statements:

All assigned hazard statements should appear on the label. The Competent Authority may choose to specify the order in which they appear.

	Location of GHS Information on the Label:
	The GHS hazard pictograms, signal word and hazard statements should be located together on the label. The Competent Authority may choose to provide a specified layout for the presentation of these and for the presentation of precautionary information, or allow supplier discretion.
	Supplemental Information:
	The competent authority has the discretion to allow the use of supplemental information subject to the parameters outlined in. The competent authority may choose to specify where this information should appear on the label or allow supplier discretion. In either approach, the placement of supplemental information should not impede identification of GHS information.

HAZARD DETERMINATION/CLASSIFICATION
Comparison -The NEW GHS and HCS Hazard determination/classification are self-classification processes. As classification is more involved in the GHS. The NEW GHS includes weight of evidence in the hazard determination. The OLD HCS has a one positive study threshold.

OLD – HCS- 29 CFR 1910.1200	NEW –GHS- The Globally Harmonized System for Hazard Communication.
Appendix B Hazard determination. (mandatory)	**Available data, test methods and test data quality**
The quality of a hazard communication program is largely dependent upon the adequacy and accuracy of the hazard determination. The hazard determination requirement of this standard is performance-oriented. Chemical manufacturers, importers, and employers evaluating chemicals are not required to follow any specific methods for determining hazards, but they must be able to demonstrate that they have adequately ascertained the hazards of the chemicals produced or imported in accordance with the criteria set forth in this Appendix. For purposes of this standard, the following criteria shall be	The GHS itself does not include requirements for testing substances or mixtures. Therefore, there is no requirement under the GHS to generate test data for any hazard class. It is recognized that some parts of regulatory systems do require data to be generated (e.g. pesticides), but these requirements are not related specifically to the GHS. The criteria established for classifying a mixture will allow the use of available data for the mixture itself and /or similar mixtures and /or data for ingredients of the mixture. The classification of a chemical substance or mixture depends both on the criteria and on the reliability of the test methods underpinning the criteria In some cases the classification is determined by a pass or fail of a specific test, (e.g. the ready biodegradation test for substances or ingredients of

used in making hazard determinations that meet the requirements of this standard.

"Carcinogenicity:" As described in paragraph(d)(4) of this section and Appendix A of this section, a determination by the National Toxicology Program, the International Agency for Research on Cancer, or OSHA that a chemical is a carcinogen or potential carcinogen will be considered conclusive evidence for purposes of this section. In addition, however, all available scientific data on carcinogenicity must be evaluated in accordance with the provisions of this Appendix and the requirements of the rule.

"Adequacy and reporting of data." The results of any studies which are designed and conducted according to established scientific principles, and which report statistically significant conclusions regarding the health effects of a chemical, shall be a sufficient basis for a hazard determination and reported on any material safety data sheet. In vitro studies alone generally do not form the basis for a definitive finding of hazard under the

mixtures), while in other cases, interpretations are made from dose/response curves and observations during testing. In all cases, the test conditions need to be standardized so that the results are reproducible with a given chemical substance and the standardized test yields "valid" data for defining the hazard class of concern. In this context, validation is the process by which the reliability and the relevance of a procedure are established for a particular purpose.

Tests that determine hazardous properties, which are conducted according to internationally recognized scientific principles, can be used for purposes of a hazard determination for health and environmental hazards. The GHS criteria for determining health and environmental hazards are test method neutral, allowing different approaches as long as they are scientifically sound and validated according to international procedures and criteria already referred to in existing systems for the hazard of concern and produce mutually acceptable data. Test methods for determining physical hazards are generally more clear-cut, and are specified in the GHS.

Both positive and negative results are assembled together in the weight of evidence determination. However, a single positive study performed according to good scientific principles and with statistically and biologically significant positive results may justify classification.

HCS since they have a positive or negative result rather than a statistically significant finding. The chemical manufacturer, importer, or employer may also report the results of other scientifically valid studies which tend to refute the findings of hazard.	
"Human data:" Where available, epidemiological studies and case reports of adverse health effects shall be considered in the evaluation.	**Evidence from humans** For classification purposes, reliable epidemiological data and experience on the effects of chemicals on humans (e.g. occupational data, data from accident databases) should be taken into account the evaluation of human health hazards of a chemical. Testing on humans solely for hazard identification purposes is generally not acceptable.
Not addressed in HCS	**Animal welfare** The welfare of experimental animals is a concern. This ethical concern includes not only the alleviation of stress and suffering but also, in some countries, the use and consumption of test animals. Where possible and appropriate, tests and experiments that do not require the use of live animals are preferred to those using sentient live experimental animals. To that end, for certain hazards (skin and eye irritation/corrosion or serious damage) testing schemes starting with non-animal observations/measurements are included as part of the classification system. For other hazards, such as acute toxicity, alternative animal tests, using fewer animals or causing less suffering

	are internationally accepted and should be preferred to the conventional LD_{50} test.
"Animal data:" Human evidence of health effects in exposed populations is generally not available for the majority of chemicals produced or used in the workplace. Therefore, the available results of toxicological testing in animal populations shall be used to predict the health effects that may be experienced by exposed workers. In particular, the definitions of certain acute hazards refer to specific animal testing results.	
Hazard evaluation is a process which relies heavily on the professional judgment of the evaluator, particularly in the area of chronic hazards. The performance-orientation of the hazard determination does not diminish the duty of the chemical manufacturer, importer or employer to conduct a thorough evaluation, examining all relevant data and producing a scientifically defensible evaluation	**Expert judgment** -The approach to classifying mixtures includes the application of expert judgment in a number of areas in order to ensure existing information can be used for as many mixtures as possible to provide protection for human health and the environment. Expert judgment may also be required in interpreting data for hazard classification of substances, especially where weight of evidence determinations are needed.
Hazard evaluation is a process which relies heavily on the professional judgment of the evaluator, particularly in the area of chronic hazards.	**Previously classified chemicals**. One of the general principles established by the IOMC-CG-HCCS states that test data already generated for the classification of chemicals under the existing systems

The performance-orientation of the hazard determination does not diminish the duty of the chemical manufacturer, importer or employer to conduct a thorough evaluation, examining all relevant data and producing a scientifically defensible evaluation	should be accepted when classifying these chemicals under the harmonized system thereby avoiding duplicative testing and the unnecessary use of test animals. This policy has important implications in those cases where the criteria in the GHS are different from those in an existing system. In some cases, it may be difficult to determine the quality of existing data from older studies. In such cases, expert judgment will be needed.
Hazard Determination Decomposition products which are produced during the normal use of the product or in foreseeable emergencies (e.g., plastics which are injection molded, diesel fuel emissions) are covered. An employer may rely upon the hazard determination performed by the chemical manufacturer. Normally, the chemical manufacturer possesses knowledge of hazardous intermediates, by-products, and decomposition products that can be emitted by their product. Any substance which is inextricably bound in a product is not covered under the HCS. For example, a hazard determination for a product containing crystalline silica may reveal that it is bound in a rubber elastomer and under	**Substances / Mixtures posing special problems** The effect of a substance or mixture on biological and environmental systems is influenced, among other factors, by the physicochemical properties of the substance or mixture and/or ingredients of the mixture and the way in which ingredient substances are biologically available. Some groups of substances may present special problems in this respect, for example, some polymers and metals. A substance or mixture need not be classified when it can be shown by conclusive experimental data from internationally acceptable test methods that the substance or mixture is not biologically available. Similarly, bio availability data on ingredients of a mixture should be used where appropriate in conjunction with the harmonized classification criteria when classifying mixtures.

normal conditions of use or during foreseeable emergencies cannot become airborne and, therefore, cannot present an inhalation hazard. In such a situation, the crystalline silica need not be indicated as a hazardous ingredient since it cannot result in employee exposure.	
"Adequacy and reporting of data." The results of any studies which are designed and conducted according to established scientific principles, and which report statistically significant conclusions regarding the health effects of a chemical, shall be a sufficient basis for a hazard determination and reported on any material safety data sheet. In vitro studies alone generally do not form the basis for a definitive finding of hazard under the HCS since they have a positive or negative result rather than a statistically significant finding. The chemical manufacturer, importer, or employer may also report the results of other scientifically valid studies which tend to refute the findings of hazard.	**Weight of evidence**-For some hazard classes, classification results directly when the data satisfy the criteria. For others, classification of a substance or a mixture is made on the basis of the total weight of evidence. This means that all available information bearing on the determination of toxicity is considered together, including the results of valid in vitro tests, relevant animal data, and human experience such as epidemiological and clinical studies and well-documented case reports and observations. The quality and consistency of the data are important. Evaluation of substances or mixtures related to the material being classified should be included, as should site of action and mechanism or mode of action study results. Both positive and negative results are assembled together in A single weight of evidence determination. Positive effects which are consistent with the criteria for classification in each chapter, whether seen in humans or animals, will normally justify classification. Where evidence is available from both

	sources and there is a conflict between the findings, the quality and reliability of the evidence from both sources must be assessed in order to resolve the question of classification. Generally, data of good quality and reliability in humans will have precedence over other data. However, even well-designed and conducted epidemiological studies may lack sufficient numbers of subjects to detect relatively rare but still significant effects, or to assess potentially confounding factors. Positive results from well-conducted animal studies are not necessarily negated by the lack of positive human experience but require an assessment of the robustness and quality of both the human and animal data relative to the expected frequency of occurrence of effects and the impact of potentially confounding factors. Route of exposure, mechanistic information and metabolism studies are pertinent to determining the relevance of an effect in humans. When such information raises doubt about relevance in humans, a lower classification may be warranted. When it is clear that the mechanism or mode of action is not relevant to humans, the substance or mixture should not be classified.

II. Comparison of Health Hazards –

The NEW GHS has several health hazard endpoints, e.g., mutagenicity and target organ systemic toxicity that do not exactly correspond to the OLD HCS hazards. In general the major difference between the HCS and the GHS is untested mixtures.

OSHA has a single 1% cut-off value for all health hazards, except carcinogens at 0.1%. These cut-off values require labels, MSDSs, and disclosure of Hazardous components. In the NEW GHS cut-off values for mixtures vary by endpoint. The GHS cut-off values for labeling, MSDSs and disclosure can be different. The NEW GHS acute toxicity and irritant hazard determinations for mixtures have more steps.

III. Comparison of Physical Hazards –

The NEW GHS physical hazards are defined by criteria that specify a test method. Physical hazards data may not be available or may not have been obtained by the specified test method. For several physical hazard endpoints the HCS criteria is a definition.

The NEW GHS has multiple subcategories within an endpoint. These subcategories lead to specific signal words, hazard phrases and pictograms. For substances previously classified under the HCS, existing data should be accepted when the substances are classified under the GHS.

EXPLOSIVES	
Comparison -The OLD HCS has only one hazard category for Explosives and the NEW GHS has **6** hazard categories. The value of multiple hazard categories for the work place should be addressed. The HCS does not require testing nor specify test methods.	
HCS Criteria	**GHS Criteria**
Test Method -HCS has no Test Method. **Definition** –"Explosive" means a chemical that causes a sudden, almost instantaneous release of pressure, gas, and heat when subjected to sudden shock, pressure, or high temperature.	**Test Method** -UN Manual of Tests and Criteria Part I Test Series 2 to 7 -Recommended tests for Explosives (incl. Articles) 2(a) UN Gap test 2(b) Koenen test 2(c) Time/Pressure test 3(a)(ii) BAM Fallhammer 3(b)(i) BAM Friction apparatus 3(c) Thermal Stability test at 75°C 3(d) Small-scale burning test 4(a) Thermal Stability test for unpackaged articles and packaged articles 4(b)(i) Steel tube drop test for liquids 4(b)(ii) Twelve meter drop test for unpackaged articles, packaged articles and packaged substances 5(a) Cap sensitivity test 5(b)(ii) USA DDT test 5(c) External fire test for Division 1.5 6(a) Single package test 6(b) Stack test 6(c) External fire (bonfire) test 7(a) EIDS cap test 7(b) EIDS gap test 7(c)(ii) Friability test 7(d)(i) EIDS bullet impact test 7(e) EIDS external fire test 7(f) EIDS slow cook-off test 7(g) 1.6 Article external fire test 7(h) 1.6 Article slow cook-off test 7(j) 1.6 Article bullet impact-off test 7(k) 1.6 Article stack test

Definition -Explosive substance means a solid or liquid substance (or mixture of substances) which is in itself capable by chemical reaction of producing gas at such a temperature and pressure and at such a speed as to cause damage to the surroundings. Pyrotechnic substances are included even when they do not evolve gases.

Criteria -Substances, mixtures and articles of this class are assigned to one of six divisions 1.1 to 1.6depending on the type of hazard they present:

Division1.1 Substances and articles which have a mass explosion hazard (a mass explosion one which affects almost the entire load virtually instantaneously);
Division 1.2 Substances and articles which have a projection hazard but not a mass explosion hazard;
Division 1.3 Substances and articles which have a fire hazard and either a minor blast hazard or a minor projection hazard or both, but not a mass explosion hazard:
1. combustion of which gives rise to considerable radiant heat; or
(ii) which burn one after another, producing minor blast or projection effects or both;
Division 1.4 Substances and articles which present no significant hazard: Substances and articles which present only a small hazard in the event of ignition or initiation. The effects are largely confined to the package and no projection of fragments of appreciable size or range is to be expected. An external fire shall not cause virtually instantaneous explosion of almost the entire contents of the package;
1.5 Very insensitive substances which have a

	mass explosion hazard: substances which have a mass explosion hazard but are so insensitive that there is very little probability of initiation or of transition from burning to detonation under normal conditions; Division1.6 Extremely insensitive articles which do not have a mass explosion hazard: articles which contain only extremely insensitive detonating substances and which demonstrate a negligible probability of accidental initiation or propagation. NOTE: Substances that are too unstable for allocation to the above divisions are also to be classified as explosive.

FLAMMABLE GASES
Comparison -The OLD HCS has one hazard category for Flammable Gases. The NEW GHS has **2** hazard categories. The HCS does not require testing nor specify test methods.

OLD HCS Criteria	NEW GHS Criteria
Test Method	**Test Method**
HCS has no Test method.	ISO 10156:1996
Definition-	**Definition-**
"Gas, flammable" means: (A) A gas that, at ambient temperature and pressure, forms a flammable mixture with air at a concentration of	Flammable gas means a gas having a flammable range with air at 20 °C and a standard pressure of 101.3 kPa. **Criteria-**

thirteen (13) percent by volume or less; or (B) A gas that, at ambient temperature and pressure, forms a range of flammable mixtures with air wider than twelve (12) percent by volume, regardless of the lower limit;	Substance sand mixtures of this hazard class are assigned to one of two hazard categories on the basis of the outcome of the test or calculation method: 1. Gases, Which at 20°C and a standard pressure of 101.3kPa: (a) Are ignitable when in a mixture of 13% or less by volume in air; or 1. Have a flammable range with air of at least 12 percentage points regardless of the lower flammable limit. 2. Gases, other than those of category 1, which, at 20°C and a standard pressure of 101.3kPa, have a flammable range while mixed in air.

FLAMMABLE AEROSOLS

Comparison -The OLD HCS has one hazard class/category for Flammable Aerosols. The NEW GHS has **2** hazard categories.

OLD HCS Criteria	NEW GHS Criteria
Test Method 16 CFR 1500.45 **Definition** "Aerosol, flammable" means an aerosol that, when tested by the method described in	**Test Method** GHS Document Annex 11 **Definition** -Aerosols means any non-refillable receptacles made of metal, glass or plastics and containing a gas compressed, liquefied or dissolved under pressure, with or without a liquid, paste or powder, and fitted with a release device allowing the contents to be ejected as solid or liquid particles in suspension in a gas, as a foam, paste or powder or in a liquid state or in a gaseous state. Aerosol includes aerosol dispensers.

| 16 CFR 1500.45, yields a flame projection exceeding 18 inches at full valve opening, or a flashback (a flame extending back to the valve) at any degree of valve opening; | **Criteria** -Substances and mixtures of this hazard class are assigned to one of two hazard categories on the basis of their components, i.e.: flammable liquids (see GHS Chapter 2.6); flammable gases (see GHS Chapter 2.2). flammable solids (see GHS Chapter 2.7); and, if applicable, the results of the foam test (for foam aerosols) and of the ignition distance test and enclosed space test (for spray aerosols): NOTE: Flammable components do not cover pyrophoric, self-heating or water-reactive substances because such components are never used as aerosol contents. The chemical heat of combustion (DHc), in kilojoules per gram (kJ/g), is the product of the theoretical heat of combustion (D Hcomb), and a combustion efficiency, usually less than 1.0 (a typical combustion efficiency is 0.95 or 95%.). For a composite aerosol formulation, the chemical heat of combustion is the summation of the weighted heats of combustion for the individual components, as follows: DH_c (product)= S[I% x $DH_{c(I)}$] where: DH_c = chemical heat of combustion (kJ/g) I% = weight fraction of component I in the product $DH_{c(I)}$ =chemical heat of combustion of component I (kJ/g). The chemical heats of combustion can be found in literature, calculated or determined by tests (see ASTM D 240, ISO/FDIS 13943:1999 (E/F) 86.I to 86.3 and NFPA 30B). |

OXIDIZING GASES	
Comparison -The OLD HCS covers Oxidizers as a class of chemicals with one category. The NEW GHS covers Oxidizers by physical state with 1 hazard category for gases.	
OLD HCS Criteria	**NEW GHS Criteria**
Test Method HCS has no Test Method. Definition "Oxidizer" means a chemical other than a blasting agent or explosive as defined in1910.109(a), that initiates or promotes combustion in other materials, thereby causing fire either of itself or through the release of oxygen or other gases.	Test Method ISO 10156:1996 Definition Oxidizing gas means any gas which may, generally by providing oxygen, cause or contribute to the combustion of other material more than air does. Criteria Substances and mixtures of this hazard class are assigned to a single hazard category on the basis that, generally by providing oxygen, they cause or contribute to the combustion of other material more than air does.

GASES UNDER PRESSURE	
Comparison -The OLD HCS has one hazard class/category for Compressed Gases. The NEW GHS uses physical state as a basis for **4** groups.	
OLD HCS Criteria	**NEW GHS Criteria**
Test Method HCS has no test method.	**Test Method**-For this group of gases, the following information is required to be

Definition -
"Compressed gas" means:
(i) A gas or mixture of gases having, in a container, an absolute pressure exceeding 40 psi at 70 deg. F (21.1 deg. C); or
(ii) A gas or mixture of gases having, in a container, an absolute pressure exceeding 104 psi at 130 deg. F (54.4 deg. C) regardless of the pressure at 70 deg. F (21.1 deg. C); or
(iii) A liquid having a vapor pressure exceeding 40 psi at100 deg. F (37.8 deg. C) as determined by ASTM D-323-72.

known:
• The vapor pressure at 50°C
• The physical state at 20°Cat standard ambient pressure
• The critical temperature.
Data can be found in literature, calculated or determined by testing. Most pure gases are already classified in the UN Model Regulations.

Criteria -Gases are classified, according to their physical state when packaged, into one of four groups as follows:

Compressed gases; A gas which when packaged under pressure is entirely gaseous at-50°C; including all gases with a critical temperature < -50°C.

Liquefied gases; A gas which when packaged under pressure is partially liquid at temperatures above -50°C. A distinction is made between:
i) High pressure liquefied gas: a gas with a critical temperature between -50°C and-+65°C; and
ii) Low pressure liquefied gas: a gas with a critical temperature above +65°C
Refrigerated liquefied gases
A gas which when packaged is made partially liquid because of its low temperature.

Dissolved gases -A gas which when packaged under pressure is dissolved in a liquid phase solvent..The critical temperature is the temperature above which a pure gas cannot be liquefied, regardless of the degree of compression.

FLAMMABLE LIQUIDS	
Comparison -The OLD HCS has two hazard categories for Flammable Liquids that cover the same flash point range as the **4** GHS categories.	
OLD HCS Criteria	**NEW GHS Criteria**
Test Method Flash point: (i) Tagliabue Closed Tester (See American National Standard Method of Test for Flash Point by Tag Closed Tester, Z11.24-1979(ASTM D 56-79)) for liquids with a viscosity of less than 45 Saybolt Universal Seconds (SUS) at 100 deg. F (37.8 deg. C), that do not contain suspended solids and do not have a tendency to form a surface film under test; or	**Test Method** -Flash Point is determined by closed cup methods as provided in GHS Chapter 2.5, paragraph 11. Initial Boiling Point is also required **Definition** -Flammable liquid means a liquid having a flash point of not more than 93 °C. **Criteria** -Substances and mixtures of this hazard class are assigned to one of four hazard categories on the basis of the flash point and boiling point:
(ii) Pensky-Martens Closed Tester (see American National Standard Method of Test for Flash Point by Pensky-Martens Closed Tester,Z11.7-1979 (ASTM D 93-79)) for liquids with a viscosity equal to or greater than 45 SUS at 100 deg. F (37.8 deg. C), or that contain suspended solids, or that have a tendency to form a surface film under test; or	1. Flash point < 23°C& initial boiling point < 35°C 2 . Flash point < 23°C& initial boiling point > 35°C 3. Flash point >23°C and < 60°C 4. Flash point > 60°C and< 93°C Gas oils, diesel and light heating oils in the flash point range of 55°C to 75°C may be regarded as a special group for some regulatory purposes. Liquids with a flash point of more than 35°C may be regarded as non-flammable liquids for some regulatory
(iii) Seta flash Closed Tester (see American National Standard	purposes (e.g. transport) if negative

| Method of Test for Flash Point by Seta flash Closed Tester (ASTM D3278-78)).

Definition

"Liquid, flammable" means any liquid having a flashpoint below 100 deg. F (37.8 deg. C), except any mixture having components with flashpoints of 100 deg. F (37.8 deg. C) or higher, the total of which make up 99 percent or more of the total volume of the mixture. | results have been obtained in the sustained combustibility test L.2of the UN Manual of Tests and Criteria Part III.

Viscous flammable liquids such as paints, enamels, lacquers, varnishes, adhesives and polishes may be regarded as a special group for some regulatory purposes (e.g. transport). The classification or the decision to consider these liquids as non-flammable may be determined by the pertinent regulation or competent authority. |

FLAMMABLE SOLIDS

Comparison –The OLDHCS has one hazard class/category for Flammable Solids. The NEW GHS has **2** hazard categories.

OLD HCS Criteria	NEW GHS Criteria
Test Method 16 CFR 1500.44	**Test Method** -UN Manual of Tests and Criteria Part III Test N.1
Definition "Solid, flammable" means a solid, other than a blasting agent or explosive as defined in 1910.109(a), that is liable to cause fire through friction, absorption of moisture, spontaneous chemical change, or retained heat from manufacturing or processing, or which can be ignited readily and when ignited burns so vigorously and persistently as to create a serious hazard. A chemical shall be considered to be a flammable solid if, when tested by the method described in 16 CFR 1500.44, it ignites and burns with a self-sustained flame at a rate greater than one-tenth of an inch per second along its major axis.	**Definition**-Flammable solid means a solid which is readily combustible, or may cause or contribute to fire through friction. **Criteria** -Substances and mixtures of this hazard class are assigned to one of two hazard categories on the basis of the outcome of the test: 1 Burning rate test: Substances other than metal powders: - wetted zone does not stop>fire and - burning time < 45 seconds or burning rate > 2.2mm/second Metal powders: - burning time ≤ 5 minutes r> 2 Burning rate test: Substances other than metal powders: - wetted zone stops the fire for at least 4 minutes and - burning time < 45 seconds or burning rate > 2.2mm/second Metal powders: - burning time > 5 minutes and < 10 minutes

SELF REACTIVE SUBSTANCES	
Comparison- The OLD HCS has only one hazard category for Self-Reactive (Unstable/Reactive) Substances. The NEW GHS has **7** hazard categories. The value of multiple hazard categories for the workplace should be addressed.	
OLD HCS Criteria	**NEW GHS Criteria**
Test Method HCS has no Test Method. Definition "Unstable (reactive)" means a chemical which in the pure state, or as produced or transported, will vigorously polymerize, decompose, condense, or will become self-reactive under conditions of shocks, pressure or temperature.	**Test Method**-UN Manual of Tests and Criteria Part II Test Series A to H Recommended tests for Self Reactive Substance A.6 UN Detonation test B 1 Detonation test in package C.1 Time/Pressure test C.2 Deflagration test D.1 Deflagration test in the package E.1 Koenen test E.2 Dutch pressure vessel test F.4 Modified Trauzl test G.1 Thermal explosion test in package H.1 United States SADT test (for packages) H.2 Adiabatic storage test (for packages etc) H.4 Heat accumulation storage test (for packages IBCs and small tanks)) Preliminary Safety Assessment Tests - Falling weight test for impact sensitivity - Friction or impacted friction test for friction sensitivity - test to assess Thermal Stability and the exothermic decomposition energy - test to assess the effect of ignition **Definition** -Self-reactive substance means a thermally unstable liquid or solid substance liable to undergo a strongly exothermic decomposition even without participation of oxygen (air). This definition excludes

<table>
<tr><td></td><td>

substances or mixtures classified under the GHS as explosive, organic peroxides or as oxidizing.

Criteria-Substances and mixtures of this hazard class are assigned to one of the seven 'Types' A to G on the basis of the outcome of the tests.Any self-reactive substance should be considered for classification in this class unless:

(a)　They are explosives, according to the GHS criteria of Chapter2.1;

(b)　They are oxidizing substances, according to the GHS criteria of Chapters 2.13 or 2.14;

(c)　They are organic peroxides, according to the GHS criteria of Chapter 2.15;

(d)　Their heat of decomposition is < 300 J/g; or

(e)　Their self-accelerating decomposition temperature (SADT) is> 75°C for 50kg package.

Self-reactive substances are classified in one of the seven categories of "types A to G" for this class, according to the following principles:

(A)　Any self-reactive substance which can detonate or deflagrate rapidly, as packaged, will be defined as self-reactive substance Type A

(B)　Any self-reactive substance possessing explosive properties and which, as packaged, neither detonates nor deflagrates rapidly, but is liable to undergo a thermal explosion in that package will be defined as self-reactive substance TYPE B;

(C)　Any self-reactive substance possessing explosive properties when the substance as packaged cannot detonate or deflagrate rapidly or undergo a thermal explosion will be defined as self-reactive substance TYPE C;

(D)　Any self-reactive substance which in laboratory testing:

</td></tr>
</table>

	(i) detonates partially, does not deflagrate rapidly and shows no violent effect when heated under confinement; or (ii) does not detonate at all, deflagrates slowly and shows no violent effect when heated under confinement; or (iii) does not detonate or deflagrate at all and shows a medium effect when heated under confinement; will be defined self-reactive substance TYPE D; (E) Any self-reactive substance which, in laboratory testing, neither detonates nor deflagrates at all and shows low or no effect when heated under confinement will be defined as self-reactive substance TYPE E; (F) Any self-reactive substance which, in laboratory testing, neither detonates in the cavitated state nor deflagrates at all and shows only a low or no effect when heated under confinement as well as low or no explosive power will be defined self-reactive substance TYPE F; 1. Any self-reactive substance which, in laboratory testing, neither detonates in the cavitated state nor deflagrates at all and shows no effect when heated under confinement nor any explosive power, provided that it is thermally stable (self-accelerating decomposition temperature is 60°C to 75°C for a 50kg package), and, for liquid mixtures, a diluent having a boiling point not less than 150°C is used for desensitization will be defined as self-reactive substance TYPE G. If the mixture is not thermally stable or a diluent having a boiling point less than 150°C is used for desensitization, the mixture shall be defined self-reactive substance TYPE F

PYROPHORIC LIQUIDS

Comparison -The OLD HCS has one hazard class/category for Pyrophorics. The NEW GHS covers Pyrophorics by physical state with **one** hazard category for Pyrophoric liquids.

OLD HCS Criteria	NEW GHS Criteria
Test Method	**Test Method** -UN Manual of Tests and Criteria Part III Test N.3
HCS has no Test Method.	**Definition** -Pyrophoric liquid means a liquid which, even in small quantities, is liable of igniting within five minutes after coming into contact with air.
Definition	
"Pyrophoric" means a chemical that will ignite spontaneously in air at a temperature of 130 deg. F (54.4 deg. C) or below.	**Criteria** -Substances and mixtures of this hazard class are assigned to a single hazard category on the basis of the outcome of the test: The liquid ignites within 5minutes when added to an inert carrier and exposed to air, or it ignites or chars a filter paper on contact with air within 5 minutes.

PYROPHORIC SOLIDS

Comparison –The OLD HCS has one hazard class/category for Pyrophorics. The NEW GHS covers Pyrophorics by physical state with **one** hazard category for Pyrophoric solids.

OLD HCS Criteria	NEW GHS Criteria
Test Method HCS has no Test Method.	**Test Method**-UN Manual of Tests and Criteria Part III Test N.2
Definition	**Definition** -Pyrophoric solid means a solid which, even in small quantities, is liable of igniting within

"Pyrophoric" means a chemical that will ignite spontaneously in air at a temperature of 130 deg. F (54.4 deg. C) or below.	five minutes after coming into contact with air. **Criteria** -Substances and mixtures of this hazard class are assigned to a single hazard category on the basis of the outcome of the test: The solid ignites within 5 minutes of coming into contact with air.

SELF HEATING SUBSTANCES

Comparison -The OLD HCS does not have this exact hazard class. According to the GHS building blocks, OSHA will need to determine if this hazard class will be in the HCS.

OLD HCS Criteria	**NEW GHS Criteria**
Test Method HCS has no Test Method. Definition "Unstable (reactive)" means a chemical which in the pure state, or as produced or transported, will vigorously polymerize, decompose, condense, or will become self-reactive under conditions of shocks, pressure or temperature. Or "Pyrophoric" means a chemical that will ignite spontaneously	**Test Method** -UN Manual of Tests and Criteria Part III Test N.4 **Definition**-Self-heating substance means a solid or liquid substance, other than a pyrophoric substance, which, by reaction with air and without energy supply, is liable to self-heat; this substance differs from a pyrophoric substance in that it will ignite only when in large amounts (kilograms) and after long periods of time (hours or days). **Criteria** -Substances and mixtures of this hazard class are assigned to one of two hazard categories on the basis of the outcome of the test: 1 A positive result is obtained in a test using a 25 mm sample cube at 140°C 2 (a) A positive result is obtained in a test using a 100 mm sample cube at 140°C and a negative result is obtained in a test using a 25 mm cube sample at 140°C and the substance is to be packed in packages with a volume of more than 3 m^3; or

in air at a temperature of 130 deg. F (54.4 deg. C) or below.	(b) A positive result is obtained in a test using a 100 mm sample cube at 140°C and a negative result is obtained in a test using a 25 mm cube sample at 140°C, a positive result is obtained in a test using a 100 mm cube sample at 120°C and the substance is to be packed in packages with a volume of more than 450litres; or (c) A positive result is obtained in a test using a 100 mm sample cube at 140°C and a negative result is obtained in a test using a 25 mm cube sample at 140°C and a positive result is obtained in a test using a 100 mm cube sample at 100°C.

Substances which on Contact with Water emits Flammable Gases
Comparison -The OLD HCS has one hazard class/category for Water Reactive. The NEW GHS has **3** hazard categories. The HCS does not require testing nor specify test methods.

OLD HCS Criteria	NEW GHS Criteria
Test Method HCS has no Test method. Definition "Water-reactive" means a chemical that reacts with water to release a gas that is either flammable or presents a health hazard.	**Test Method** UN Manual of Tests and Criteria Part III Test N.5 **Definition** -Substance which, in contact with water, emit flammable gases means a solid or liquid substance or mixture which, by interaction with water, is liable to become spontaneously flammable or to give off flammable gases in dangerous quantities. **Criteria**-Substances and mixtures of this hazard class are assigned to one of three hazard categories on the basis of the outcome of the test: 1. Any substance which reacts vigorously with water at ambient temperatures and demonstrates generally a tendency for the gas produced to ignite spontaneously, or which reacts readily with

	water at ambient temperatures such that the rate of evolution of flammable gas is equal to or greater than 10 liters per kilogram of substance over any one minute. 2. Any substance which reacts readily with water at ambient temperatures such that the maximum rate of evolution of flammable gas is equal to or greater than 20 liters per kilogram of substance per hour, and which does not meet the criteria for category 1. 3. Any substance which reacts slowly with water at ambient temperatures such that the maximum rate of evolution of flammable gas is equal to or greater than 1 liter per kilogram of substance per hour, and which does not meet the criteria for categories 1 and 2.

OXIDIZING LIQUIDS	
Comparison - The OLD HCS covers Oxidizers as a class of chemicals with one category. The NEW GHS covers Oxidizers by physical state with **3 NEW** hazard categories for liquids.	
OLD HCS Criteria	**NEW GHS Criteria**
Test Method-HCS has no Test Method.	**Test Method**-UN Manual of Tests and Criteria Part III Test O.2
Definition -"Oxidizer" means a chemical other than a blasting agent or explosive as defined in 1910.109(a) that initiates or promotes combustion in other materials thereby causing fire either of itself or through the release of oxygen or other gases.	**Definition**-Oxidizing liquid means a liquid which, while in itself not necessarily combustible, may, generally by yielding oxygen, cause, or contribute to, the combustion of other material. **Criteria**-Substances and mixtures of this hazard class are assigned to one of three hazard categories on the basis of the outcome of the test: 1. Any substance which, in the 1:1 mixture, by mass, of substance and cellulose tested, spontaneously ignites; or the mean pressure rise time of a 1:1 mixture, by mass, of substance and cellulose is less than that of a 1:1 mixture, by mass, of 50% perchloric acid and cellulose. 2. Any substance which, in the 1:1 mixture, by mass, of substance and cellulose tested, exhibits a mean pressure rise time less than or equal to the mean pressure rise time of a 1:1 mixture, by mass, of 40% aqueous sodium chlorate solution and cellulose; and the criteria for category 1 are not met. 3. Any substance which, in the 1:1 mixture, by mass, of substance and cellulose tested, exhibits a mean pressure rise time less than or equal to

	the mean pressure rise time of a 1:1 mixture, by mass, of 65% aqueous nitric acid and cellulose; and the criteria for category 1 and 2 are not met.

OXIDIZING SOLIDS

Comparison -The OLD HCS covers Oxidizers as a class of chemicals with one category. The NEW GHS covers Oxidizers by physical state with **3** NEW hazard categories for solids.

OLD HCS Criteria	NEW GHS Criteria
Test Method HCS has no Test Method. Definition "Oxidizer" means a chemical other than a blasting agent or explosive as defined in 1910.109 (a), that initiates or promotes combustion in other materials, thereby causing fire either of itself or through the release of oxygen or other gases.	**Test Method** -UN Manual of Tests and Criteria Part III Test O.1 **Definition** -Oxidizing solid means a solid which, while in itself not necessarily combustible, may, generally by yielding oxygen, cause, or contribute to, the combustion of other material. Criteria Substances and mixtures of this hazard class are assigned to one of three hazard categories on the basis of the outcome of the test: 1. Any substance which, in the 4:1 or 1:1 sample-to-cellulose ratio (by mass) tested, exhibits a mean burning time less than the mean burning time of a 3:2 mixture, by mass, of potassium bromate and cellulose. 2. Any substance which, in the 4:1 or 1:1 sample-to-cellulose ratio (by mass) tested, exhibits a mean burning time equal to or less than the mean burning time of a 2:3 mixture (by mass) of potassium bromate and cellulose and the criteria for category 1 are not met. 3. Any substance which, in the 4:1 or 1:1

<table>
<tr>
<td></td>
<td>sample-to-cellulose ratio (by mass) tested, exhibits a mean burning time equal to or less than the mean burning time of a 3:7 mixture (by mass) of potassium bromate and cellulose and the criteria for categories 1and 2 are not met.</td>
</tr>
</table>

ORGANIC PEROXIDES

Comparison –The OLD HCS covers Organic Peroxides as a class of chemicals with one category. The NEW GHS has **7** hazard categories for Organic Peroxides. The value of multiple hazard categories for the workplace should be addressed.

OLD HCS Criteria	NEW GHS Criteria
Test Method HCS has no Test Method. Definition "Organic peroxide" means an organic compound that contains the bivalent - O-O-structure and which may be considered to be a structural derivative of hydrogen peroxide where one or both of the hydrogen atoms has been replaced by an organic radical.	**Test Method** -UN Manual of Tests and Criteria Part II Test Series A to H Recommended tests for Organic Peroxides A.6 UN Detonation test B 1 Detonation test in package C.1 Time/Pressure test C.2 Deflagration test D.1 Deflagration test in the package E.1 Koenen test E.2 Dutch pressure vessel test F.4 Modified Trauzl test G.1 Thermal explosion test in package H.1 United States SADT test (for packages) H.2 Adiabatic storage test (for packages etc) H.4 Heat accumulation storage test (for packages IBCs and small tanks)) Preliminary Safety Assessment Tests - Falling weight test for impact sensitivity - Friction or impacted friction test for friction sensitivity - test to assess thermal stability and the exothermic decomposition energy - test to assess the effect of ignition

Definition -Organic peroxide means a liquid or solid organic substance which contains the bivalent -0-0- structure and may be considered a derivative of hydrogen peroxide, where one or both of the hydrogen atoms have been replaced by organic radicals. The term also includes organic peroxide formulation (mixtures).

Criteria-Substances and mixtures of this hazard class are assigned to one of the seven 'Types' A to G on the basis of the outcome of the tests: Any organic peroxide is considered for classification in this class, unless it contains:

(a)   Not more than 1.0% available oxygen from the organic peroxides when containing not more than 1.0% hydrogen peroxide; or

(b)   Not more than 0.5% available oxygen from the organic peroxides when containing more than 1.0% but not more than 7.0% hydrogen peroxide text-transform:uppercase'>Note: The available oxygen content (%) of an organic peroxide mixture is given by the formula:
$16 \times S\ (n_i \times c_i/m_i)$
where: n_i = number of per oxygen groups per molecule of organic peroxide i;
c_i = concentration (mass %) of organic peroxide i;
m_i = molecular mass of organic peroxide i
Organic peroxides are classified in one of the seven hazard categories of "types A to G" for this class, according to the following principles:

(A) Any organic peroxide mixture which can detonate or deflagrate rapidly, as packaged, will be defined as organic peroxide TYPE A;

(B) Any organic peroxide mixture possessing explosive properties and which, as packaged, neither detonates nor deflagrates rapidly, but is liable to undergo a thermal explosion in that package will be defined as organic peroxide TYPE B;

(C) Any organic peroxide mixture possessing explosive properties when the substance as packaged cannot detonate or deflagrate rapidly or undergo a thermal explosion will be defined as organic peroxide TYPE C;

(D) Any organic peroxide mixture which in laboratory testing:

(i) detonates partially, does not deflagrate rapidly and shows no violent effect when heated under confinement; or
(ii) does not detonate at all, deflagrates slowly and shows no violent effect when heated under confinement; or
(iii) does not detonate or deflagrate at all and shows a medium effect when heated under confinement;
will be defined as organic peroxide TYPE D;

(E) Any organic peroxide mixture which, in laboratory testing, neither detonates nor deflagrates at all and shows low or no effect when heated under confinement will be defined as organic peroxide TYPE E;

(F) Any organic peroxide mixture which, in laboratory testing, neither detonates in the cavitated state nor deflagrates at all and shows

	only a low or no effect when heated under confinement as well as low or no explosive power will be defined as organic peroxide TYPE F;
	(G) Any organic peroxide mixture which, in laboratory testing, neither detonates in the cavitated state nor deflagrates at all and shows no effect when heated under confinement nor any explosive power, provided that it is thermally stable (self-accelerating decomposition temperature is 60°Or higher for a 50 kg package), and, for liquid mixtures, a diluent having a boiling point of not less than 150°C is used for desensitization, will be defined as organic peroxide TYPE G. If the mixture is not thermally stable or a diluent having a boiling point less than 150°C is used for desensitization, the mixture shall be defined as organic peroxide TYPE F. Type G has no hazard communication elements assigned but should be considered for properties belonging to other hazard classes. Types A to G may not be necessary for all systems.

SUBSTANCES CORROSIVE TO METAL	
Comparison -The OLD HCS does not regulate Substances Corrosive to Metal. According to the GHS building block approach, OSHA needs to determine if the HCS will cover this hazard class in the future.	
OLD HCS Criteria	**NEW GHS Criteria**
Test Method HCS has no Test Method or Criteria/Definition. Definition HCS does not cover this classification. HCS Appendix A states: This term shall not refer to action on inanimate surfaces.	**Test Method:** Steel: ISO9328 (II): 1991 - Steel type P235 Aluminum: ASTM G31-72 (1990) -- non-clad types 7075-T6or AZ5GU-T66 **Definition**-Corrosive to metal means a substance or a mixture which by chemical action will materially damage, or even destroy, metals. **Criteria**-Corrosion rate on steel or aluminum surfaces exceeding6.25 mm per year at a test temperature of 55°C. A substance that is corrosive to metal is classified in A single hazard category for this class on the basis of the test.

LABEL EXAMPLES:

The GHS label requirements are a significant change from performance-oriented HCS labels. Examples can be useful visual illustrations to understand what is being described verbally. Several label examples are included in this comparison. The ANSI Z 129.1, Hazardous Industrial Chemicals-Precautionary Labeling, label format has been used for the OSHA HCS label format.

EXAMPLE 1: Label for Small workplace container (10 liter) packaged inside an outer shipping container -- for workplace audience.

Hazards (Liquid): flammable liquid, flash point = 120° F; oral LD50 = 275 mg/kg

EXAMPLE 2: Label for Medium size company.

Hazards (Liquid): moderate skin and eye irritant, possible cancer hazard by inhalation.

EXAMPLE 3: Label for Large container (200 liter drum) for transport, emergency response and workplace audiences.

Hazards (Liquid mixture): classified under GHS as toxic to reproduction, category 1B and flammable liquid, category 3. UN RTDG classification is flammable liquid - UN 1263.

** Competent Authorities may choose not to require disclosure of ingredient identities on the label of products intended only for workplace use.

EXAMPLE # 1 - NEW GHS Label.

ToxiFlam

Danger!
Toxic if swallowed
Flammable liquid and vapor
**Contains: XYZ

Do not taste or swallow. Get medical attention. Do not take internally. Wash thoroughly after handling. Keep away from heat, sparks and flame. Keep container closed. Use only with adequate ventilation.

FIRST AID

If swallowed, induce vomiting immediately, as directed by medical personnel. Never give anything by mouth to an unconscious person.

See Material Safety Data Sheet for further details regarding safe use of this product.

Company name, Address, Phone number

**Competent Authorities may choose not to require disclosure of ingredient identities on the label of products intended only for workplace use.

EXAMPLE # 2 - NEW GHS Label.

My Product
Warning!
Cause Skin And Eye Irritation
Suspected of causing cancer by inhalation
**Contains: XYZ

Do not breathe vapors or mist. Use only with adequate ventilation. Avoid contact with eyes, skin and clothing. Wash thoroughly after handling

FIRST AID:

EYES: Immediately flush eyes with plenty of water for at least 15 minutes. Get medical attention. SKIN: In case of contact, immediately flush skin with plenty of water. Remove contaminated clothing and shoes. Wash clothing before reuse. Get medical attention if irritation develops and persists.

Company name, Address, Phone number

**CompetentAuthorities may choose not to require disclosure of ingredient identities on the label of products intended only for workplace use.

EXAMPLE # 3 –NEW GHS Label for large container (200 liter drum) for transport, emergency response and workplace audiences.

ZZZ Red Paint
Danger!
May damage fertility or the unborn child
Highly flammable liquid and vapor
**Contains lead pigments and cellosolve acetate

Keep away from heat and ignition sources. Keep away from food and drink. Avoid contact with skin and eyes and inhalation of vapor. Wash hands thoroughly after use and before eating

FIRST AID

For skin contact, remove contaminated clothing and wash affected area thoroughly with water. If irritation develops, seek medical attention. For eye contact, immediately flush eyes with flowing water for at least 15 minutes and seek medical attention.

GHS Example PLC, Leeds, England. Telephone# 44 999 999 9999

Competent Authorities may choose not to require disclosure of ingredient identities on the label of products intended only for workplace use.

– CHAPTER 3 –

What are the New Changes in the GHS/Hazard Communication Standard?

Chapter Highlights:

- **Re-classification of all Chemicals;**
- **Changing the name from Material Safety Data Sheets to Safety Data Sheets;**
- **Training Workers on new Labels and SDS Sheets;**
- **The GHS Labeling Requirements are Specific: Signal Words, Hazard Statements, and Pictograms;**
- **The use of Pictograms is a significant change for USA Workplace Labeling.**

INTRODUCTION- *Background of the Regulation*

The Occupational Safety and Health Administration (OSHA) is revising the Hazard Communication Standard (HCS) to make it consistent with the Global Harmonized System for Classification and Labeling of Chemicals (GHS). When OSHA first promulgated the HCS in 1983, it applied only to the manufacturing sector of the economy. In 1987, the Agency expanded the coverage of the standard to all industries, including construction and maritime. The HCS requires chemical manufacturers and importers to evaluate the hazards of the chemicals they produce or import and specifies the health and physical criteria that must be used to classify the hazards. Chemical manufacturers and importers are also required to communicate the hazard information to the users of chemicals by preparing and distributing material safety data sheets (MSDSs) and putting labels on containers containing the chemicals.

The information transmitted under the HCS requirements provides the foundation upon which a chemical safety and health program can be built in the workplace. The old HCS standard was performance-oriented; that is, it establishes requirements for labels and safety data sheets but does not provide the specific language to convey the information

or the format in which to provide it. However, the new Standard is very specific.

The impetus for the GHS arose due to both domestic and international regulatory concerns. There were two main problems. First, the thresholds used to classify chemicals are sometimes different from one country to another and from one Federal agency to another. As a result, chemicals often get classified into entirely different hazard classes by different entities.

In the US, for instance, some chemicals are classified as "explosive" under DOT regulations; while under OSHA regulations they are not (or, vice versa). Such differences are known to cause confusion among workers who read both DOT and OSHA labels and cannot easily determine what precautionary steps they must take while handling, distributing, and storing hazardous chemicals. One of the objectives of the GHS-compliant regulations is to remove such confusion and make the management of chemicals more efficient.

The differences in hazard classifications among countries also give rise to considerable inefficiencies. They often require companies to maintain multiple chemical management databases, hire teams of professionals to keep track of the conflicting regulatory requirements, and produce labels and SDSs containing varying information. And, it is even more problematic to translate them into multiple languages. Second, the performance-oriented requirements of the HCS that do not specify how the information should be presented in SDSs have led manufacturers to provide widely varying and confusing information about identical chemicals. The users of the chemicals have long complained about the non-uniformity of the information provided in SDSs and labels. Labels containing unfamiliar pictograms (hazard symbols), hazard statements, or other information have added to the confusion among those using, handling, and storing hazardous chemicals. The new standard would require that the content and format of SDSs and labels for workplace chemicals conform to the uniform GHS requirements.

New Criteria for Classification of Chemicals

Hazard Classes
Hazard classes describe the physical characteristics of chemical substances on the one hand (explosives, flammable solids, oxidizing gases) and health hazards (acute oral toxicity, carcinogenicity, reproductive toxicity, etc.) on the other hand. The new HCS/GHS regulation makes only minor changes to the number and type of hazard classes. Figure 3.1 shows all but one of the physical hazard classes is included in the current regulation. Similarly, Figure 3.2 shows all but one health hazard class, *Hazard Categories*

The new regulation makes substantial changes to the number of hazard categories within each hazard class. As shown in Figure 3.2 shows that the regulation has several hazard classes are likely to be subdivided into more hazard categories. For example, it would be possible to divide Acute Toxicity into 5 hazard categories, Skin Corrosion into 3 hazard categories, and Skin Irritation into 2 hazard categories. Further, the Eye Irritation class would be divided into 2 categories and Carcinogenicity of a chemical can be within three ranges. The practical effect of this differentiation would be to more accurately define the hazard of chemicals.

Figure 3.1 - Coverage of Physical Hazards

Physical Hazard Classes	Old HCS	New GHS
Explosives	(1) x	(6)
Flammable Gases	(1) x	(2)
Flammable Aerosols	(1) x	(2)
Oxidizing Gases	(1) x	(1)
Gases under Pressure	(1) x	(4)
Flammable Liquids	(2) x	(4)
Flammable Solids	(1) x	(2)
Self-Reactive Substances	(1) x	(7)
Pyrophoric Liquids	(1) x	(1)
Pyrophoric Solids	(1) x	(1)
Self-Heating	(1) x	(1)
Oxidizing Liquids	(1) x	(3)
Oxidizing Solids	(1) x	(3)
Organic Peroxides	(1) x	(7)
Corrosive to Metals		(1)
Substances which in Contact with Water Emit Gases	(1) x	(3)

Footnote-1 x indicates the presence of a hazard class. The number within the ( ) is equal to the number of Hazard Categories. Thus, Explosives under GHS are classified into six hazard categories.

Figure 3.2 - Coverage of Health Hazards

Health Hazard Classes	Old HCS	New GHS
Acute Toxicity	(2) x	(5)
Skin Corrosion	(1) x	(up to 3)
Skin Irritation	(1) x	(up to 2)
Skin Sensitization	(1) x	(1)
Serious Eye Damage	(1) x	(1)
Eye Irritation	(2) x	(2)
Respiratory Sensitization	(1) x	(1)
Mutagenicity	(1) x	(3)
Carcinogenicity	(1) x	(3)
Reproductive Toxicology	(1) x	(3)
	(1) x	(1)
Oxidizing Liquids	(1) x	(3)
Oxidizing Solids	(1) x	(3)
Organic Peroxides	(1) x	(7)
Corrosive to Metals		(1)
Substances which in Contact with Water Emit Gases	(1) x	(3)

Footnote - 1 x indicates the presence of a hazard category. The number within the ( ) is equal to the number of Hazard Categories. Thus, Acute Toxicity under GHS is classified into five hazard categories.

Treatment of Mixtures

The new GHS/HCS regulation makes substantial changes to the procedures by which mixtures are evaluated under the current regulation. The changes will enable the hazards of mixtures to be more accurately defined. No additional testing will be required to classify mixtures. Producers of mixtures will be able to use the same data to classify mixtures as are used to classify pure chemicals if such data specific to the mixture are available. In addition, the proposed standard allows producers to apply a flexible set of bridging principles to classify mixtures based on the classifications of the ingredients. The bridging principles also allow many different mixtures with variations in their ingredients to be classified relatively easily. Mixtures can be classified by comparing the nature of their formulations to other mixtures that have already been classified.

Changes in Hazard Classes and Criteria, and Procedures for Classification

As discussed above, there are three (1) changes in hazard classes,(2) changes in hazard categories, and (3) changes in procedures for application of the hazard criteria. The changes in hazard classes for physical hazards are not expected to impose additional costs, because the necessary data are generally available and are used under DOT and voluntary industry standards. The data for the new health hazard class "Effects on or via Lactation" are already covered indirectly under the current regulation.

The application of the criteria for classifying chemicals into specific hazard categories is likely to involve some additional work compared to what would normally be done to update and revise the information and classifications required under the existing standard. The application of the criteria may be done manually if a company produces only a small number of chemicals substances. Many companies in the past have conducted the calculations manually. However, if a company produces a large number of chemical substances including mixtures, it is likely to use large databases to manage its chemicals and conduct computerized calculations to classify its products.

What are the New Changes in the Labels?

The new HCS/GHS regulation will have very specific label requirements. The Pictograms will help provide employers the appropriate and relevant information. The following nine hazard pictograms which will be used in the New Hazcom/GHS standard.

Each one of the Pictograms is also explained in more detail in this chapter. All of the symbols, aside from the environment symbol, are part of the standard symbols used in Hazcom/GHS regulation.

Figure 3.3

Flame	Flame over circle	Exploding bomb
Corrosion	Gas cylinder	Skull and crossbones
Exclamation mark	Environment	Health Hazard

What are Symbols/Pictograms under the New Hazcom Standard?

Symbols serve several important functions in warning labels. Symbols may alert the user to a hazard more effectively than text alone: "Symbols may be more salient than text because of visual differentiations of shape, size, and color. Usually symbols have unique details and possess more differences in appearance than do the letters of the alphabet. Letters are highly familiar and are more similar to one another than most graphical symbols." Symbols also can bolster a text message and improve label comprehension, people with low literacy, and those who do not understand the language in which the label text is written.

All symbols are not created equal. Some studies have found slower processing, poorer recognition, and greater learning difficulties with symbols versus with text—particularly if the symbols are complex or non-intuitive. These results speak to the need to choose symbols carefully and to train users on what they mean.

The Hazcom standard uses two types of symbols on chemical labels: a hazard pictogram and a precautionary pictogram. The hazard pictogram is taken from a standard set, based on the health or physical hazard class of the chemical. The precautionary pictogram depicts a measure to be taken to minimize or prevent adverse effects. Some of the benefits of symbols are:

- Symbols generally make warning labels more noticeable and easier to comprehend. They are often the most easily recalled elements of labels.

- Symbols can improve label comprehension among children, people with low literacy, and those who do not understand the language.

- Many GHS pictograms are widely recognized, but some others are more obscure.

- Symbols are most effective when there is a direct relationship between the image and the meaning, requiring minimal inference.

- Symbols tend to be most effective when paired with redundant or reinforcing text.

GHS Information required on a New Hazard Communication label:

1. Signal Words – Signal words are generally recognized as a key alerting element of warning labels. Signal words also convey a particular level of hazard. The signal word is a word that typically appears near the top of a warning, sometimes in all capital letters.

Studies of English-speaking people around the world have found a generally consistent hierarchy of signal words with respect to perceived hazard. **DEADLY, DANGER**, and **WARNING** seem to connote different levels of hazard, while the perceived difference between **WARNING** and **CAUTION** is often insignificant.

Signal words used in GHS are for example, "**Danger" and "Warning**." Danger is the more severe hazard categories while "Warning" is used for the less severe. Signal words are assigned to each hazard category.

2. Hazard Statements -A phrase assigned to a hazard class and category that describes the nature of the hazards of a hazardous product, including when appropriate, the degree of the hazard. For example, toxic in contact with skin, Causes serious eye irritation, and fatal if inhaled.

3. Precautionary Statements -Phrase (and/or pictogram) that describes the recommended measures that should be taken to minimize or prevent adverse effects resulting from exposure to a hazardous product. GHS label should include appropriate precautionary information, the choice of which belongs to the labeler or competent authority. For example, Do not eat, drink or smoke when using this product, Contaminated work clothing should not be allowed out of the workplace, **Read label before use.**

4. Product Identifier -Product identifier should be used and it should match product identifier used on the SDS. If mixture is covered by UN Model regulations for transport of Dangerous goods, UN proper shipping name should also appear on package

Label for substance should include the chemical identity of the substance. Label should include chemical identities of all ingredients or alloying elements that contribute to acute toxicity, skin corrosion or serious eye damage, germ cell mutagenicity, carcinogenicity, reproductive toxicity, skin or respiratory sensitization, or specific target organ toxicity (STOT). When these hazards appear on the label

Where a substance or mixture is supplied exclusively for workplace use, competent authority may choose to give suppliers discretion to include chemical identities on the SDS, in lieu of including them on labels.

5. Supplier Identification -Name, address and
telephone number of the manufacturer or supplier of the substance or mixture should be provided on the label.

6. Hazard Pictograms -A pictogram means a
graphical composition that includes a symbol plus other graphic elements, such as a border, background pattern or color that is intended to convey specific information. There are 9 symbols used in the pictograms: **1).Flame, 2).Flame over circle, 3).Exploding bomb, 4).Corrosion, 5).Gas cylinder, 6) Skull and crossbones, 7).Exclamation point, 8).Environment and, 9). Health hazards.**

All hazard pictograms used in the GHS should be in the shape of a square set at a point. Pictograms prescribed by the GHS should have a black symbol on a white background with a red frame sufficiently wide to be clearly visible. However, when such a pictogram appears on a label for a package which will not be exported, the Competent Authority may choose to give suppliers and employers discretion to use a black border.

What is Required on Workplace Labeling?

Products falling within the scope of the GHS will carry the GHS label at the point where they are supplied to the workplace, and that label should be maintained on the supplied container in the workplace. The GHS label or label elements should also be used for workplace containers. However, the competent authority can allow employers to use alternative means of giving workers the same information in a different written or displayed format when such a format is more appropriate to the workplace and communicates the information as effectively as the GHS label.

They are required to "ensure that each container of **hazardous chemicals** leaving the workplace is labeled, tagged or marked" with labels that contain:

- **Identity of the hazardous chemical(s), and**
- **Appropriate hazard warnings**

If you put chemicals in a secondary container or re-bottle chemicals at your facility, it is critical that you have a good secondary label program to ensure the chemicals are properly identified. Label requirements under GHS are different then what the HCS traditionally required. GHS labels use six standardized elements: product identifier, manufacture information, signal words, pictograms, hazard statements, and precautionary statements. See above.

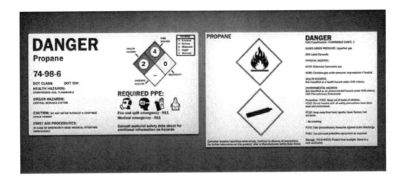

Figure 3.4 – Labels on Secondary Containers.

Label information could be displayed in the work area, rather than on the individual containers. Alternative means of providing workers with the information contained in GHS labels are needed usually where hazardous chemicals are transferred from an original supplier container into a workplace container or system, or where chemicals are produced in a workplace but are not packaged in containers intended for sale or supply. Chemicals that are produced in a workplace may be contained or stored in many different ways such as: small samples collected for testing or analysis, piping systems including valves, process or reaction vessels, or cars, conveyer systems or free-standing bulk storage of solids.

In batch manufacturing processes, one mixing vessel may be used to contain a number of different chemical mixtures. In many situations, it is impractical to produce a complete GHS label and attach it to the container, due, for example, to container size limitations or lack of access to a process container. Some examples of workplace situations where chemicals may be transferred from supplier containers include: containers for laboratory testing or analysis, storage vessels, piping or process reaction systems or temporary containers where the chemical will be used by one worker within a short timeframe. Decanted chemicals intended for immediate use could be labeled with the main components and directly refer the user to the supplier label information and **SDS.**

Updating Labels

All systems should specify a means of responding in an appropriate and timely manner to new information and updating labels and SDS information accordingly. The following are examples of how this will be achieved.

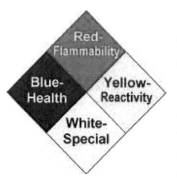

Suppliers should respond to "new and significant" information they receive about a chemical hazard by updating the label and safety data sheet for that chemical. New and significant information is any information that changes the GHS classification of the substance or mixture and leads to a resulting change in the information provided on the label or any information concerning the chemical and appropriate control measures that may affect the SDS.

This could include, for example, new information on the potential adverse chronic health effects of exposure as a result of recently published documentation or test results, even if a change in classification may not yet be triggered.

Updating should be carried out promptly on receipt of the information that necessitates the revision. The competent authority may choose to specify a time limit within which the information should be revised. This applies only to labels and SDS for products that are not subject to an approval mechanism such as pesticides.

Suppliers should also periodically review the information on which the label and safety data sheet for a substance or mixture is based, even if no new and significant information has been provided to them in respect of that substance or mixture. This will require a search of chemical hazard databases for new information. The competent authority may choose to specify a time (typically 3 – 5 years) from the date of original preparation, within which suppliers should review the labels and SDS information.

Target Audiences

The GHS takes into consideration the needs of the target audience that will be the primary end-users of the harmonized communication scheme as well as the manner in which these audiences will receive and use the information. Those audiences include:

Workplace:

- Employers and workers need to know about the specific hazards related to the chemicals used or handled in the workplace, and about specific protective measures required to avoid adverse effects.
- Packaging and storing of a chemical can minimize hazards, however, workers and emergency responders need to know mitigation factors are appropriate in case of an accident they may require information that can be read at a distance.
- In addition to the label, additional information is available to workers through the SDSs and workplace risk management system.

Consumers:

- The label is likely to be the sole source of information readily available to the consumer.
- Consumer education is more difficult and less efficient than education for other audiences.
- The issue of comprehensibility is of particular importance for this target audience since they may rely solely on label information.

Emergency responders:

- Emergency responders need information on a range of levels, including accurate, detailed and sufficiently clear information to facilitate an immediate response.

- Fire fighters need information that can be seen and understood at a distance, such as graphical and coded information.

Transport:

- Wide-range of target audiences, especially transport workers and emergency responders.
- Information needed by different transport workers is dependent upon the type of work done and amount of contact they will have with hazardous items.
- Drivers may need only limited information unless they are also responsible for the loading and unloading of packages and/or filling of tanks.

1. Skull and Crossbones

This is the symbol that will appear on the most severely toxic chemicals. Depending on the toxicity of the chemical, the skull and crossbones indicate that the chemical may be toxic or fatal. Specifically it can mean:

- **Fatal if swallowed**
- **Fatal in contact with skin**
- **Fatal if inhaled**
- **Toxic if swallowed**
- **Toxic in contact with skin**
- **Toxic if swallowed**

This chart below summarizes the hazard criteria for the category(s) in each class for the **Skull and Crossbones** pictogram to appear on a product label. It also lists the corresponding hazard statement and signal word that will accompany the pictogram.

Hazard Class/ Category	Criteria	Hazard Communication Elements	
Acute Toxicity **Category 1**	$LD_{50} \leq 5$ mg/kg bodyweight (oral) $LD_{50} \leq 50$ mg/kg bodyweight (skin/dermal) $LC_{50} \leq 100$ ppm (gas) $LC_{50} \leq 0.5$ (mg/l) (vapor) $LC_{50} \leq 0.05$ (mg/l) (dust, mist)	Symbol	
		Signal Word	Danger
		Hazard Statement	Fatal if swallowed (oral) Fatal in contact with skin (dermal)Fatal if inhaled (gas, vapor, dust, mist)
Acute Toxicity **Category**	LD_{50} between 5 and less than 50 mg/kg	Symbol	

2	bodyweight (oral)	Signal Word	Danger
	LD_{50} between 50 and less than 200 mg/kg bodyweight (skin/dermal)	Hazard Statement	Fatal if swallowed (oral)
	LC_{50} between 100 and less than 500 ppm (gas)		Fatal in contact with skin (dermal)
	LC_{50} between 0.5 and less than 2.0 (mg/l) (vapor)		Fatal if inhaled (gas, vapor, dust, mist)
	LC_{50} between 0.05 and less than 0.5 (mg/l) (dust, mist)		
Acute Toxicity **Category 3**	LD_{50} between 50 and less than 300 mg/kg bodyweight (oral)	Symbol	
	LD_{50} between 200 and less than 1000 mg/kg		

bodyweight (skin/dermal)	Signal Word	Danger
LC_{50} between 500 and less than 2500 ppm (gas)	Hazard Statement	Toxic if swallowed (oral)
LC_{50} between 2.0 and less than 10.0 (mg/l) (vapor)		Toxic in contact with skin (dermal)Toxic if inhaled (gas, vapor, dust, m
LC_{50} between 0.5 and less than 1.0 (mg/l) (dust, mist)		

2. Exclamation Mark

This is the symbol that will appear on chemicals with less severe toxicity. Depending on the health hazard, it can mean:

- **Harmful if swallowed**
- **Harmful in contact with skin**
- **Harmful if inhaled**
- **Causes skin irritation**
- **Causes serious eye irritation**
- **May cause allergic skin reaction**

The chart below summarizes the hazard criteria for the category(s) in each class for the **Exclamation mark** pictogram to appear on a product label. It also lists the corresponding hazard statement and signal word that will accompany the pictogram.

Hazard Category	Criteria	Hazard Communication Elements	
Acute toxicity **4**	LD_{50} between 300 and less than 2000 mg/kg bodyweight (oral)	Symbol	**!**
	LD_{50} between 1000 and less than 2000 mg/kg bodyweight (skin/dermal)	Signal Word	Warning
	LC_{50} between 2500 and less than 5000 ppm (gas) LC_{50} between 10.0 and less than 20.0 (mg/l) (vapor) LC_{50} between 1.0 and less than 5.0 (mg/l) (dust, mist)	Hazard Statement	Harmful if swallowed (oral)Harmful in contact with skin(dermal)Harmful if inhaled (gas, vapor, dust, mist)

Skin Corrosion / Irritation **2**	1. For substances and tested mixtures • Human experience or data showing reversible damage to the skin following exposure of up to 4 hours; • Structure/activity or structure property relationship to a substance or mixture already classified as an irritant; • Positive results in a valid and accepted *in vitro* skin irritation test; or • Animal experience or test data that indicate that the substance/mixture causes reversible damage to the skin following exposure of up to 4 hours, mean value of ≥ 2.3 < 4.0 for erythema/eschar or for oedema, or	Symbol	!
		Signal Word	Warning
		Hazard Statement	Causes skin irritation

	inflammation that persists to the end of the observation period, in 2 of 3 tested animals . 2. If data for a mixture are not available, use bridging principles. 3. If bridging principles do not apply, classify as an irritant if: (a) For mixtures where substances can be added: the sum of concentrations of corrosive substances in the mixture is ≥ 1% but ≤5%; the sum of the concentrations of irritant substances is > 10%; or the sum of (10 × the concentrations of corrosive ingredients) + (the concentrations of irritant ingredients) is ≥ 10%; or (b) For mixtures where substances cannot be added:≥ 3%.		
Serious eye damage/e ye	1. For substances and tested mixtures • Classification as	Symbol	!

irritation	severe skin irritant; • Human experience or data showing production of changes in the eye which are fully reversible within 21 days; • Structure/activity or structure property relationship to a substance or mixture already classified as an eye irritant; • Positive results in a valid and accepted *in vitro* eye irritation test; or • Animal experience or test data that indicate that the substance/mixture produces a positive response in at least 2 of 3 tested animals of: corneal opacity ≥ 1, iritis ≥ 1, or conjunctival edema (chemosis) ≥ 2.	Signal Word	Warning
2A		Hazard Statement	Causes Serious Eye Irritation
	2. If data for a mixture		

	are not available, use bridging principles in 3.3.3.2. 3. If bridging does not apply, classify as an irritant (2A) if: (a) For mixtures where substances can be added: the sum of the concentrations of skin and/or eye Category 1 substances in the mixture is ≥ 1% but ≤ 3%; the sum of the concentrations of eye irritant substances is ≥ 10%; or the sum of (10 × the concentrations of skin and/or eye category 1 substances) + (the concentrations of eye irritants) is ≥ 10%; (b) For mixtures where substances cannot be added: the sum of the concentrations of eye irritant ingredients is 3%.		
Skin sensitizer **1**	1. For substances and tested mixtures • If there is evidence in humans that the individual substance can	Symbol	!
		Signal	Warning

induce sensitization by skin contact in a substantial number of persons, or • Where there are positive results from an appropriate animal test. 2. If the mixture meets the criteria set forth in the "Bridging Principles" through one of the following: (a) Dilution; (b) Batching; (c) Substantially similar mixture. 3. If bridging principles do not apply, classify if any individual skin sensitizer in the mixture has a concentration of: ≥ 1.0% Solid/Liquid/Gas	Word		
	Hazard Statement	May cause allergic skin reaction

3. Corrosion

This is the symbol that will appear on chemicals that have corrosive properties. Depending on the properties of the chemical(s) in the product, the corrosion pictogram can mean:

- **May be corrosive to metals**
- **Causes severe skin burns and eye damage**
- **Causes serious eye damage**

The chart below summarizes the hazard criteria for the category(s) in each class for the corrosion pictogram to appear on a product label. It also lists the corresponding hazard statement and signal word that will accompany the pictogram.

Hazard Class/ Category	Criteria	Hazard Communication Elements	
Corrosive to metals **Category 1**	Corrosion rate on steel or aluminum surfaces exceeding 6.25 mm per year at a test temperature of 55 °C.	Symbol	
		Signal Word	Warning
		Hazard	May be corrosive to

		Statement	metals
Skin corrosion / irritation **Category 1**	1. For substances and tested mixtures: • Human experience showing irreversible damage to the skin; • Structure/activity or structure property relationship to a substance or mixture already classified as corrosive; • pH extremes of ≤ 2 and ≥ 11.5 including acid/alkali reserve capacity; • Positive results in a valid and accepted *in vitro* skin corrosion test; or • Animal experience or test data that indicate that the substance/mixture causes irreversible damage to the skin following exposure of up to 4 hours . 2. If data for a mixture are not available, use bridging	Symbol	
		Signal Word	Danger
		Hazard Statement	Causes severe skin burns and eye damage

	principles. 3. If bridging principles do not apply, (a) For mixtures where substances can be added: Classify as corrosive if the sum of the concentrations of corrosive substances in the mixture is ≥ 5% (for substances with additives); or (b) For mixtures where substances cannot be added: ≥ 1%.		
Serious eye damage/ irritation **Category 1**	*For substances and tested mixtures* • Classification as corrosive to skin; • Human experience or data showing damage to the eye which is not fully reversible within 21 days; • Structure/activity or structure property relationship to a substance or mixture already classified as corrosive; • pH extremes of < 2 and > 11.5	Symbol	
		Signal Word	Warning
		Hazard Statement	Causes serious eye damage

	including buffering capacity; • Positive results in a valid and accepted *in vitro* test to assess serious damage to eyes; or • Animal experience or test data that the substance or mixture produces either (1) in at least one animal, effects on the cornea, iris or conjunctiva that are not expected to reverse or have not reversed; or (2) in at least 2 of 3 tested animals a positive response of corneal opacity ≥ 3 and/or iritis.2. If data for a mixture are not available, use bridging principles if bridging principles do not apply(a) For mixtures where substances can be added: Classify as Category 1 if the sum of the concentrations of substances classified as corrosive to the skin and/or eye Category 1 substances in the		

	mixture is ≥ 3%.		

4. Environment

 This is the symbol that will appear on chemicals which are acutely hazardous to Fish, Crustacea, or aquatic plants. The environment pictogram can mean:

- **Very toxic to aquatic life**

  The chart below summarizes below the hazard criteria for the category(s) in each class for the environment pictogram to appear on a product label. It also lists the corresponding hazard statement and signal word that will accompany the pictogram.

Hazard Class/ Category	Criteria	Hazard Communication Elements	
Acute Toxicity **Categor y** **1**	1. For substances and tested mixtures: $L(E)C_{50} \leq 1mg/1$ where $L(E)C_{50}$ is either fish 96hr LC50, crustacea 48hr EC LC_{50} or aquatic plant 72 or 96hr ErC_{50}.	Symbol	
	2. If data for a mixture are not available, use bridging	Signal	Warning

principles .	Word	
3. If bridging principles do not apply, (a) For mixtures with classified ingredients: The summation method (see reveals: [Concentration of Acute 1] × M > 25% where M is a multiplying factor . (b) For mixtures with tested ingredients: The additivity formula is below: • $L(E)C_{50} \leq 1mg/l.$ (c) For mixtures with both classified and tested ingredients: The combined additives formula and summation method is below: • Concentration of Acute 1 × M > 25%. 4. For mixtures with no usable information for one or more relevant ingredients, classify using the available information and add the statement: "x percent of the mixture consists of component(s) of unknown hazards to the aquatic environment".	Hazard Statement	Very toxic to aquatic life

5. Flame

This is the symbol that will appear on chemicals that are **Flammable**. Depending on the properties of the chemical(s) and the product, the flame can mean:

- **Extremely flammable gas**
- **Extremely flammable aerosol**
- **Flammable aerosol**
- **Extremely flammable liquid and vapor**
- **Highly flammable liquid and vapor**
- **Flammable liquid and vapor**
- **Flammable solid**

The chart below summarizes the hazard criteria for the category(s) in each class for the flame pictogram to appear on a pesticide product label. It also lists the corresponding hazard statement and signal word that will accompany the pictogram.

Hazard Class/ Category	Criteria	Hazard Communication Elements	
Flammable gases **Category**	Gases and gas mixtures, which at 20 °C and a standard pressure	Symbol	

1	of 101.3 kPa: (a) are ignitable when in a mixture of 13% or less by volume in air; or (b) have a flammable range with air of at least 12 percentage points regardless of the lower flammable limit.	Signal Word	Danger
		Hazard Statement	Extremely flammable gas
Flammable aerosols **Category 1**	On the basis of its components, of its chemical heat of combustion and, if applicable, of the results of the foam test, for foam aerosols, and of the ignition distance test and enclosed space test, for spray aerosols.	Symbol	
		Signal Word	Danger
		Hazard Statement	Extremely flammable aerosol

Flammable aerosols **Category 2**	On the basis of its components, of its chemical heat of combustion and, if applicable, of the results of the foam test, for foam aerosols, and of the ignition distance test and enclosed space test, for spray aerosols.	Symbol	
		Signal Word	Warning
		Hazard Statement	Flammable aerosol
Flammable liquids **Category 1**	Flash point < 23 °C and initial boiling point ≤ 35 °C.	Symbol	
		Signal Word	Danger
		Hazard Statement	Extremely flammable liquid and vapor

Flammable liquids **Category 2**	Flash point < 23 °C and initial boiling point >35 °C.	Symbol	
		Signal Word	Danger
		Hazard Statement	Highly flammable liquid and vapor
Flammable liquids **Category 3**	Flash point ≥ 23 °C and ≤ 60 °C.	Symbol	
		Signal Word	Warning
		Hazard Statement	Flammable liquid and vapor

Flammable solids Category 1	Burning rate test: Substances and mixtures other than metal powders: - wetted zone does not stop fire and< - burning time < 45 seconds or burning rate > 2.2 mm/s Metal powders: - burning time ≤ 5 minutes.	Symbol	
		Signal Word	Danger
		Hazard Statement	Flammable solid
Flammable solids Category 2	Burning rate test: Substances and mixtures other than metal powders: - wetted zone stops the fire for at least 4 minutes and - burning time < 45 seconds or burning rate > 2.2	Symbol	
		Signal Word	Warning
		Hazard Statement	Flammable solid

	mm/second		
	Metal powders:		
	- burning time > 5 minutes and ≤ 10 minutes.		

6. Flame over Circle

This is the symbol that will appear on some labels and may cause fire or explosion. Depending on the chemical. Specifically it can mean:

- **May cause or intensify fire ;oxidizer**
- **May cause fire or explosion; strong oxidizer**
- **May intensify fire; oxidizer**
- **May cause fire or explosion; strong oxidizer.**

The chart below summarizes the hazard criteria for the category(s) in each class for the **Flame over Circle** pictogram to appear on a product label. It also lists the corresponding hazard statement and signal words that will accompany the pictogram.

Hazard Class/ Category	Criteria	Hazard Communication Elements	
Oxidizing Gases Category 1	Any gas which may, generally by providing oxygen, cause or contribute to the combustion of other material more than air does.	Symbol	
		Signal Word	Danger
		Hazard Statement	May cause or intensify fire; oxidizer

Hazard Class/ Category	Criteria	Hazard Communication Elements	
Oxidizing liquids Category 1	Any substance which, in the 1:1 mixture, by mass, of substance and cellulose tested, spontaneously ignites; or the mean pressure rise time of a 1:1 mixture, by mass, of substance and cellulose is less than that of a 1:1 mixture, by mass, of 50% perchloric acid and cellulose.	Symbol	
		Signal Word	Danger
		Hazard Statement	May cause fire or explosion; strong oxidizer

Hazard Class/ Category	Criteria	Hazard Communication Elements	
Oxidizing liquids **Category 2**	Any substance which, in the 1:1 mixture, by mass, of substance and cellulose tested, exhibits a mean pressure rise time less than or equal to the mean pressure rise time of a 1:1mixture, by mass, of 40% aqueous sodium chlorate solution and cellulose; and the criteria for Category 1 are not met.	Symbol	
		Signal Word	Danger
		Hazard Statement	May intensify fire; oxidizer

Hazard Class/ Category	Criteria	Hazard Communication Elements	
Oxidizing liquids Category 3	Any substance which, in the 1:1 mixture, by mass, of substance and cellulose tested, exhibits a mean pressure rise time less than or equal to the mean pressure rise time of a 1:1mixture, by mass, of 65% aqueous nitric acid and cellulose; and the criteria for Categories 1and 2 are not met.	Symbol	
		Signal Word	Warning
		Hazard Statement	May intensify fire; oxidizer

Hazard Class/ Category	Criteria	Hazard Communication Elements	
Oxidizing solids Category 1	Any substance which, in the 4:1 or 1:1 sample-to-cellulose ratio (by mass) tested, exhibits a mean burning time less than the mean burning time of a 3:2 mixture, by mass, of potassium bromate and cellulose.	Symbol	
		Signal Word	Danger
		Hazard Statement	May cause fire or explosion; strong oxidizer

Hazard Class/ Category	Criteria	Hazard Communication Elements	
Oxidizing solids **Category** 2	Any substance which, in the 4:1 or 1:1sample-to-cellulose ratio (by mass) tested, exhibits a mean burning time equal to or less than the mean burning time of a 2:3 mixture (by mass) of potassium bromate and cellulose and the criteria for Category 1 are not met.	Symbol	
		Signal Word	Danger
		Hazard Statement	May intensify fire; oxidizer

Hazard Class/ Category	Criteria	Hazard Communication Elements	
Oxidizing solids **Category 3**	Any substance which, in the 4:1 or 1:1 sample-to-cellulose ratio (by mass) tested, exhibits a mean burning time equal to or less than the mean burning time of a 3:7 mixture (by mass) of potassium bromated and cellulose and the criteria for Categories 1 and 2 are not met.	Symbol	
		Signal Word	Warning
		Hazard Statement	May intensify fire; oxidizer

7. Exploding Bomb

This is the symbol that will appear on chemicals that mean **Explosive.** Depending on the properties of the chemical(s) and the product, the Exploding Bomb can mean:

- **Unstable explosive**
- **Explosive; mass explosion hazard**
- **Explosive; severe projection hazard**
- **Explosive; fire, blast or projection hazard**
- **Fire or projection hazard**
- **May mass explode in fire**
- **Heating may cause an explosion**

The chart below summarizes the hazard criteria for the category(s) in each class for the exploding Bomb pictogram to appear on a product label. It also lists the corresponding hazard statement and signal word that will accompany the pictogram.

Hazard Class/ Category	Criteria	Hazard Communication Elements	
Unstable explosive	According to the results of the test in Part I of the *Manual of Tests and Criteria, UN Recommendations on the Transport of Dangerous Goods.*	Symbol	
		Signal Word	Danger
		Hazard Statement	Unstable explosive

Hazard Class/ Category	Criteria	Hazard Communication Elements	
Division 1.1	According to the results of the test in Part I of the *Manual of Tests and Criteria, UN Recommendations on the Transport of Dangerous Goods.*	Symbol	
		Signal Word	Danger
		Hazard Statement	Explosive; mass explosion hazard

Hazard Class/ Category	Criteria	Hazard Communication Elements	
Division 1.2	According to the results of the test in Part I of the *Manual of Tests and Criteria, UN Recommendations on the Transport of Dangerous Goods.*	Symbol	
		Signal Word	Danger
		Hazard Statement	Explosive; severe projection hazard

Hazard Class/ Category	Criteria	Hazard Communication Elements	
Division 1.3	According to the results of the test in Part I of the *Manual of Tests and Criteria, UN Recommendations on the Transport of Dangerous Goods.*	Symbol	
		Signal Word	Danger
		Hazard Statement	Explosive; fire, blast or projection hazard

Hazard Class/ Category	Criteria	Hazard Communication Elements	
Division 1.4	According to the results of the test in Part I of the *Manual of Tests and Criteria, UN Recommendations on the Transport of Dangerous Goods.*	Symbol	
		Signal Word	Warning
		Hazard Statement	Fire or projection hazard

Hazard Class/ Category	Criteria	Hazard Communication Elements	
Division 1.5	According to the results of the test in Part I of the *Manual of Tests and Criteria, UN Recommendations on the Transport of Dangerous Goods.*	Symbol	1.5
		Signal Word	Danger
		Hazard Statement	May mass explode in fire

Hazard Class/ Category	Criteria	Hazard Communication Elements	
Division 1.6	According to the results of the test in Part I of the *Manual of Tests and Criteria, UN Recommendations on the Transport of Dangerous Goods.*	Symbol	1.6
		Signal Word	No signal word
		Hazard Statement	No hazard statement

Hazard Class/ Category	Criteria	Hazard Communication Elements	
Type A **Self-reactive substances and mixtures**	According to the results of tests in the *UN Recommendations on the Transport of Dangerous Goods, Manual of Tests and Criteria,* Part II and the application of the decision logic under 2.8.4.1 of Chapter 2.8	Symbol	
		Signal Word	Danger
		Hazard Statement	Heating may cause an explosion

Hazard Class/ Category	Criteria	Hazard Communication Elements	
Type A Organic peroxides	*According to the results of test series A to H in the UN Recommendations on the Transport of Dangerous Goods, Manual of Tests and Criteria, Part II and the application of the decision logic under 2.15.4.1 of Chapter 2.15.*	Symbol	
		Signal Word	Danger
		Hazard Statement	Heating may cause an explosion

8. Gas Cylinder

This is the symbol that will appear on some chemicals. It means **Gas under pressure** and may explode if heated. The Gas Cylinder can mean:

- Contains gas under pressure may explode if heated
- Contains refrigerated gas; and may cause cryogenic burns or injury.

The chart below summarizes the hazard criteria for the category(s) in each class for the **Gas Cylinder** pictogram to appear on a product label. It also lists the corresponding hazard statement and signal word s that will accompany the pictogram.

Hazard Class/ Category	Criteria	Hazard Communication Elements	
Compressed Gas	A gas, which when packaged under pressure is entirely gaseous at -50 °C; including all gases with a critical temperature ≤ -50 °C.	Symbol	
		Signal Word	Warning

Hazard Class/ Category	Criteria	Hazard Communication Elements	
Liquefied gas	A gas which when packaged under pressure is partially liquid at temperatures above -50 °C. A distinction is made between: (i) *High pressure liquefied gas*: a gas with a critical temperature between −50 °C and +65 °C; and (ii) *Low pressure liquefied gas*: a gas with a critical temperature above +65 °C.	Symbol	
		Signal Word	Warning
		Hazard Statement	Contains gas under pressure; may explode if heated

Hazard Class/ Category	Criteria	Hazard Communication Elements	
Refrigerated **liquefied gas**	A gas which when packaged is made partially liquid because of its low temperature.	Symbol	
		Signal Word	Warning
		Hazard Statement	Contains refrigerated gas; may cause cryogenic burns or injury.

Hazard Class/ Category	Criteria	Hazard Communication Elements	
Dissolved gas	A gas which when packaged under pressure is dissolved in a liquid phase solvent.	Symbol	
		Signal Word	Warning
		Hazard Statement	Contains gas under pressure; may explode if heated

9. Health Hazard

 This is the symbol that will appear on chemicals that have **Health Hazards.** Depending on the toxicity of the chemical, the Health Hazards indicates that the chemical can cause Breathing difficulties, may cause cancer or may cause organ damage. Specifically it can mean:

- **May cause allergic or asthmatic symptoms or breathing difficulties if inhaled.**
- **May cause genetic defects (state route of exposure if it is conclusively proven that no other routes of exposure cause the hazard).**
- **Suspected of causing genetic defects (state route of exposure if it is conclusively proven that no other routes of exposure cause the hazard).**
- **May cause cancer (state route of exposure if it is conclusively proven that no other routes of exposure cause the hazard.**
- **Suspected of causing cancer (state route of exposure if it is conclusively proven that no other routes of exposure cause the hazard).**
- **May damage fertility or the unborn child (state specific effect if known) (state route of exposure if it is conclusively proven that no other routes of exposure cause the hazard).**
- **Suspected of damaging fertility or the unborn child (state specific effect if known) (state route of exposure if it is conclusively proven that no other routes of exposure**

cause the hazard).

- Causes damage to organs (or state all organs affected, if known) (state route of exposure if it is conclusively proven that no other routes of exposure cause the hazard).
- May cause damage to organs (or state all organs affected, if known) (state route of exposure if it is conclusively proven that no other routes of exposure cause the hazard).
- May be fatal if swallowed and enters airways.
- May be harmful if swallowed and enters airways.

The charts below summarize the hazard criteria for the category(s) in each class for the **Health Hazard** pictogram to appear on a product label. It also lists the corresponding hazard statement and signal word that will accompany the pictogram.

Hazard Class/ Category	Criteria	Hazard Communication Elements	
1 **Respiratory sensitizer**	1. *For substances and tested mixtures* If there is human evidence that the individual substance induces specific respiratory hypersensitivity, and/or Where there are positive results from an appropriate animal test. 2. *If these mixture meets the criteria* set forth in the "Bridging Principles" through one of the following: (a) Dilution; (b) Batching; (c) Substantially similar mixture.	Symbol	
		Signal Word	Danger
		Hazard Statement	May cause allergic or asthmatic symptoms or breathing difficulties if inhaled

3. *If bridging principles do not apply,* classify if any individual respiratory sensitizer in the mixture has a concentration of: ε 1.0% Solid/Liquid ε 0.2% Gas		

Hazard Class/ Category	Criteria	Hazard Communication Elements	
1 Both 1A and 1B **Germ cell mutagenicity**	Known to induce heritable mutations or regarded as if it induces heritable mutations in the germ cells of humans (see criteria in 3.5.2) or mixtures containing ≥ 0.1% of such a substance.		
		Signal Word	Danger
		Hazard Statement	May cause genetic defects (state route of exposure if it is conclusively proven that no other routes of exposure cause the hazard).

Hazard Class/ Category	Criteria	Hazard Communication Elements	
2 **Germ cell mutagenicity**	Causes concern for man owing to the possibility that it may induce heritable mutations in the germ cells of humans (see criteria in 3.5.2) or mixtures containing ≥ 1.0 % of such a substance.		
		Signal Word	Warning
		Hazard Statement	Suspected of causing genetic defects (state route of exposure if it is conclusively proven that no other routes of exposure cause the hazard).

Hazard Class/ Category	Criteria	Hazard Communication Elements	
1 Both 1A and 1B **Carcinogenicity**	Known or presumed human carcinogen including mixtures containing ≥ 0.1% of such a substance.		
		Signal Word	Danger
		Hazard Statement	May cause genetic defects (state route of exposure if it is conclusively proven that no other routes of exposure cause the hazard).

Hazard Class/ Category	Criteria	Hazard Communication Elements	
2 Carcinogenicity	Suspected human carcinogen including mixtures containing more than ≥ 0.1 or ≥ 1.0 % of such a substance (see Notes 1 and 2 in Table 3.6.1 of Chapter 3.6).		
		Signal Word	Warning
		Hazard Statement	Suspected of causing cancer (state route of exposure if it is conclusively proven that no other routes of exposure cause the hazard).

Hazard Class/ Category	Criteria	Hazard Communication Elements	
1 Both 1A and 1B **Toxic to reproduction**	Known or presumed human reproductive toxicants (see criteria in section 3.7.2 of Chapter 3.7) or mixtures containing ≥ 0.1% or ≥ 0.3 % of such a substance (see section 3.7.3 and Notes 1 and 2 of Table 3.7.1, Chapter 3.7).		
		Signal Word	Danger
		Hazard Statement	May damage fertility or the unborn child (state specific effect if known) (state route of exposure if it is conclusively proven that no other routes of exposure cause the hazard).

Hazard Class/ Category	Criteria	Hazard Communication Elements	
2 **Toxic to reproduction**	Suspected human reproductive toxicants (see criteria in section 3.7.2 of Chapter 3.7) or mixtures containing ≥ 0.1% or ≥ 3.0 % of such a substance (see section 3.7.3 and Notes 3 and 4 of Table 3.7.1, Chapter 3.7).		
		Signal Word	Warning
		Hazard Statement	Suspected of damaging fertility or the unborn child (state specific effect if known) (state route of exposure if it is conclusively proven that no other routes of exposure cause the hazard).

Hazard Class/ Category	Criteria	Hazard Communication Elements	
1 **Specific target organ systemic toxicity following single exposure**	Reliable evidence on the substance or mixture (including bridging) of an adverse effect on specific organ/systems or systemic toxicity in humans or animals. May use guidance values in Table 3.8.1, Category 1 criteria as part of weight of evidence evaluation. May be named for specific organ/system. Mixture that lacks sufficient data, but contains Category 1 ingredient at a concentration of ε 1.0 to δ 10.0% for some authorities; and ε 10.0% for all authorities.	Symbol	
		Signal Word	Danger
		Hazard Statement	Causes damage to organs (or state all organs affected, if known) (state route of exposure if it is conclusively proven that no other routes of exposure cause the hazard).

Hazard Class/ Category	Criteria	Hazard Communication Elements	
2 **Specific target organ systemic toxicity following single exposure**	Evidence on the substance or mixture (including bridging) of an adverse effect on specific organ/systems or systemic toxicity from animal studies or humans considering weight of evidence and guidance values in Table 3.9.2. May be named for specific organ/system. Mixture that lacks sufficient data, but contains Category 1 ingredient: ε 1.0 but δ 10% for some authorities and contains Category 2 ingredient: ε 1.0 or ε 10%.		
		Signal Word	Warning
		Hazard Statement	May cause damage to organs (state all organs affected, if known) through prolonged or repeated exposure (state route of exposure if it is conclusively proven that no other routes of exposure cause the hazard).

Hazard Class/ Category	Criteria	Hazard Communication Elements	
1 **Specific target organ systemic toxicity following repeated exposure**	Reliable evidence on the substance or mixture (including bridging) of an adverse effect on specific organ/systems or systemic toxicity in humans or animals. May use guidance values in Table 3.9.1 as part of weight of evidence evaluation. May be named for specific organ/system. Mixture that lacks sufficient data, but contains Category 1 ingredient: ε 1 to δ 10% for some authorities; and ε 10% for all authorities.	Symbol	
		Signal Word	Danger
		Hazard Statement	Causes damage to organs (state all organs affected, if known) through prolonged or repeated exposure (state route of exposure if it is conclusively proven that no other routes of exposure cause the hazard).

Hazard Class/ Category	Criteria	Hazard Communication Elements	
2 **Specific target organ systemic toxicity following repeated exposure**	Evidence on the substance or mixture (including bridging) of an adverse effect on specific organ/systems or systemic toxicity from animal studies or humans considering weight of evidence and guidance values in Table 3.9.2. May be named for specific organ/system.		
		Signal Word	Warning
	Mixture that lacks sufficient data, but contains Category 1 ingredient: ε 1.0 but δ 10% for some authorities and contains ingredient: ε 1.0 or ε 10%.	Hazard Statement	May cause damage to organs (state all organs affected, if known) through prolonged or repeated exposure (state route of exposure if it is conclusively proven that no other routes of exposure cause the hazard).

Hazard Class/ Category	Criteria	Hazard Communication Elements	
1 **Aspiration hazard**	1. *For substances and tested mixtures* Practical experience from reliable and good quality human evidence showing human aspiration toxicity including chemical pneumonia, varying degree of pulmonary injury or death following aspiration; Hydrocarbons with a kinematic viscosity of 20.5 mm2/s or less, measured at 40 °C; 2. *If data for a mixture are not avail*able, use bridging principles in 3.10.3.2. 3. *If bridging principles do not apply*, classify under Aspiration hazard Category 1: Mixtures containing 10% or more of a	Symbol	
		Signal Word	Danger
		Hazard Statement	May be fatal If swallowed and enters airways

	substance or substances classified in Category 1 and having a kinematic viscosity of 20.5 mm2/s or less, measured at 40 °C; Mixtures which separate into two or more distinct layers, one of which contains 10 % or more of a substance or substances classified in Category 1 aspiration toxicity hazard and has a kinematic viscosity of 20.5 mm2/s or less, measured at 40 ° C.	

Hazard Class/ Category	Criteria	Hazard Communication Elements	
2 **Aspiration hazard**	1. *Substances other than those classified in Category 1* which, on the basis of animal studies and expert judgment are presumed to cause human aspiration toxicity and have a kinematic viscosity of 14 mm2/s or less, measured at 40 °C. 2. *If data for a mixture are not avai*lable, use bridging principles in 3.10.3.2. 3. *If bridging principles do not apply*, classify under Aspiration hazard Category 2: Mixtures containing 10% or more of a substance or substances classified in Category 2 and		
		Signal Word	Warning
		Hazard Statement	May be harmful if swallowed and enters airways

having a kinematic viscosity of 14 mm2/s or less, measured at 40 °C; Mixtures which separate into two or more distinct layers, one of which contains 10% or more of a substance or substances classified in Category 2 aspiration toxicity hazard and has a kinematic viscosity of 14 mm2/s or less, measured at 40 °C.		

What are the New changes in Material Safety Data Sheets?

Safety Data Sheets are an essential component of the GHS and are intended to provide comprehensive information about a substance or mixture for use in workplace chemical management. In the GHS, they serve the same function that the Material Safety Data Sheet does in OSHA's HazCom Standard. They are used as a source of info about hazards, and to obtain advice on safety precautions.

The SDS is normally product related and not specific to workplace; nevertheless, the information on an SDS enables the employer to:

Develop an Active Safety & Health Program of Worker protection measures, including training, which is specific to the workplace.

SDS also provides important source of information for other target audience in the GHS so certain elements may be used for the transport of dangerous goods, emergency responders (including poison centers), and those involved in the professional use pesticides and consumers.

SDS Preparation

The HCS requires chemical manufacturers and importers to develop an SDS for each hazardous chemical they produce or import. Chemical manufacturers and importers must provide any generally applicable precautions for safe handling and use on the SDS. They must also determine generally applicable control measures such as appropriate engineering controls, work practices, or personal protective equipment, and include that information on the SDS. Employers, in turn, must retain an SDS in the workplace for each hazardous chemical that they use and ensure that MSDSs are readily accessible to workers.

SDSs provide comprehensive hazard information, and serve as the key reference document for exposed workers and others, such as health professionals providing services to those workers. New information regarding chemical hazards or protective measures must be added to the SDS when the preparer becomes aware of this information. Updating SDSs will provide employers and workers with the most current information needed to understand the hazards associated with combustible dusts, as well as appropriate protective measures to be taken. Dissemination of this updated information is also critical to reduce exposures to combustible dusts, which have been associated with multiple incidents.

SDS Format

SDSs should provide a clear description of the data used to identify the hazards. The minimum information for each section listed below should be included. If specific information is not applicable or not available under a particular sub-heading, the SDS should clearly state this. Information in the SDS should be presented using the following 16 headings in the order below:

1. Identification of the substance or mixture and of the supplier

- GHS Product Identifier
- Other means of identification
- Recommended use of the chemical and restrictions on use
- Supplier's details (including name, address, phone number etc.)
- Emergency phone number

2. Hazard identification

- GHS classification of the substance/mixture and any national or regional information
- GHS label elements, including precautionary statements. (Hazard symbols may be provided as a graphical reproduction of the symbols in the black and white or the name of the symbol e.g. "flame", "skull and crossbones");
- Other hazards which do not result in the classification (e.g. "dust explosion hazard") or are not covered by the GHS.

3. Composition/information on ingredients

Substance

- Chemical identity;
- Common name, synonyms, etc.;
- CAS number and other unique identifiers
- Impurities and stabilizing additives which are themselves classified and which contribute to the classification of a substance.

Mixture

4. First aid measures

- Description of necessary measures, subdivided according to the different routes of exposure, i.e. inhalation, skin and eye contact and ingestion;
- Most important symptoms/effects, acute and delayed.
- Indication of immediate medical attention and special treatment needed, if necessary.

5. Fire-fighting measures

- Suitable (and unsuitable) extinguishing media.
- Specific hazards arising from the chemical (e.g. nature of any hazardous combustion products).
- Special protective equipment and precautions for fire-fighters

6. Accidental release measures

- Personal precautions, protective equipment and emergency procedures.
- Environmental precautions.
- Methods and materials for containment and cleaning up.

7. Handling and storage

- Precautions for safe handling.
- Conditions for safe storage, including any incompatibilities.

8. Exposure controls/personal protection

- Control parameters e.g. occupational exposure limit values or biological limit values.
- Appropriate engineering controls.
- Individual protection measures, such as personal protective equipment.

9. Physical and chemical properties

- Appearance (physical state, color etc.);
- Odor;
- Odor threshold;
- pH;
- Melting point/freezing point;
- Initial boiling point and boiling range;
- Flash point;
- Evaporation rate;
- Flammability (solid, gas);
- Upper/lower flammability or explosive limits;
- Vapor pressure;
- Vapor density;
- Relative density;

- Solubility(ies);
- Partition coefficient: n-octanol/water;
- Auto-ignition temperature;
- Decomposition temperature.

10. Stability and reactivity

- Reactivity;
- Chemical stability;
- Possibility of hazardous reactions;
- Conditions to avoid (e.g. static discharge, shock or vibration);
- Incompatible materials;
- Hazardous decomposition products.

11. Toxicological information- Concise but complete and comprehensible description of the various toxicological (health) effects and the available data used to identify those effects, including:

- Information on the likely routes of exposure (inhalation, ingestion, skin and eye contact);
- Symptoms related to the physical, chemical and toxicological characteristics;
- Delayed and immediate effects and also chronic effects from short and long term exposure;
- Numerical measures of toxicity (such as acute toxicity estimates).

12. Ecological information - OSHA will not be enforcing information requirements in sections 12 through 15.It is not Mandatory.

- Ecotoxicity (aquatic and terrestrial, where available);
- Persistence and degradability;
- Bioaccumulative potential;
- Mobility in the soil;
- Other adverse effects.

13. Disposal information - Description of waste residues and information on the their safe handling and methods of disposal, including the disposal of any contaminated packaging.

14. Transport information

- UN number;
- UN proper shipping name:
- Transport hazard class(es);
- Packing group, if applicable;
- Environmental hazards;
- Transport in bulk.

15. Regulatory information -Safety, health and environmental regulations specific for the product in question.

16. Other information including information on preparation and revision of the SDS Sheet -Fill in additional information as needed.

SDS Sheets

To accommodate the needs of the diverse groups who rely on MSDSs, a Standardized format has been viewed as a way to make the information on SDSs easier for users to find, and to segregate technical sections of the document from more basic elements. A standardized format was also thought to facilitate computerized information retrieval systems and to simplify employee training.

In order to develop this structure, the Chemical Manufacturers Association formed a committee to establish guidelines for the preparation of SDSs. This effort resulted in the development of American National Standards Institute (ANSI) standard Z400.1, a voluntary consensus standard for the preparation of SDSs. Employers, workers, health care professionals, emergency responders, and other SDS users participated in the development process. The standard established a 16-section format for presenting information as well as standardized headings for sections of the SDS.

By following the recommended format, the information of greatest concern to employees is featured at the beginning of the document, including information on ingredients and first aid measures. More technical information that addresses topics such as the physical and chemical properties of the material and toxicological data appears later in the document. The ANSI standard also includes guidance on the appearance and reading level of the text in order to provide a document that can be easily understood by readers.

OSHA believes that a standardized format would improve the effectiveness of SDSs. The primary basis for this belief is very simple: A consistent format would make it easier for users to find information on an SDS. Headings for SDS sections would be standardized, so SDS users would know which section to consult for the information they desire. The sections would be presented in a consistent, logical sequence to further facilitate locating information of interest. Information commonly desired by exposed employees and of greatest interest to emergency responders (*e.g.,* Hazards Identification; First Aid Measures) would be presented in the beginning of the document for easy reference. More technical information (*for example,* Stability and Reactivity &Toxicological Information) would be presented later.

By segregating more complex information on an SDS from the information that is generally easier to understand, the standardized format has the potential to address many of the concerns that have been raised regarding the comprehensibility of information on SDSs. The standardized order of information will allow SDS users who desire only basic information about a hazardous chemical to find that information without having to sift through a great deal of technical information that may have little meaning to them.

In emergency situations, rapid access to information such as first-aid measures, fire-fighting measures, and accidental release measures can be critically important. In some cases the length and complexity of MSDSs reportedly make it difficult to locate desired information on the documents.

In testimony before the U.S. Senate Subcommittee on Employment, Safety, and Training, one hospital safety director described a situation in which an employee was unable to find critical information on an MSDS in an emergency situation. **For example:**

Two gallons of the chemical xylene spilled in the lab of a hospital. By the time an employee had noticed the spill, the ventilation had already sucked most of the vapors into the HVAC. This, in turn, became suspended in the ceiling tile over the radiology department. Twelve employees were sent to the emergency room. To make the matter worse, the lab employee was frantically searching through the MSDS binder in her area for the xylene MSDS. Once she found it, she had difficulty locating the spill response section. After notifying the engineering department, she began to clean up the spill with solid waste rags, known for spontaneous combustion, and placing the rags into a clear plastic bag for disposal. She did not know that xylene has a flash point of 75 degrees Fahrenheit. She then walked the bag down to the incinerator room and left it there, basically creating a live bomb. Twelve people were treated from this exposure. The lab

employee was very upset and concerned about the safety of the affected employees and visitors, and hysterically kept stating that she could not find the necessary spill response information on the MSDS sheet.

Your company should learn a lesson from this example above. Always train your employees on MSDS Sheets and make sure they understand them.

A standardized format does not address all issues affecting SDS comprehensibility. Reading level and some design elements would continue to vary. In many respects, this is inevitable given the different target audiences that SDSs have, and the varying qualifications of those who prepare SDSs. Nevertheless, OSHA believes that the revisions will result in a substantial improvement in the quality and ease of comprehension of information provided on SDSs.Standardization would improve the accuracy of chemical hazard information indirectly. With consistent presentation of information, the task of reviewing SDSs and labels to assure accuracy would be simplified. Individuals preparing and reviewing these documents should find it easier to identify any missing elements, and compare information presented on an SDS to reference sources and other SDSs. OSHA enforcement personnel would be able to more efficiently examine SDSs when conducting inspections.

What are the New changes for Employee Information and Training?

DO NOT BLOCK

FIRE EXIT

The current regulation requires employers to "provide employees with effective information and training on hazardous chemicals in their work area at the time of their initial assignment, and whenever a new physical or health hazard the employees have not previously been trained about is introduced into their work area".

Information and training may be designed to cover categories of hazards (for example, flammability, and carcinogenicity) or specific chemicals."The current regulation also requires that employee training shall include at least "the details of the hazard communication program developed by the employer, including an explanation of the labeling system and how employees can obtain and use the appropriate hazard information."

The new regulation changes the requirements to mandate that employees be trained in **(1)** the new labels received on shipped containers and the workplace labeling system used by their employer, and **(2)** the safety data sheet including the order of information, and how employees can obtain and use the appropriate hazard information.

The GHS/OSHA Regulation Mandates 3 New Changes in Training:

1). Revise training for new employees;

2). Train employees in the new labeling for shipped containers, workplace labeling, and SDS's including the order of information on the new sds sheet; and

3). Change the written hazard communication program, to reflect the new format and content of SDSs Sheets and labels.

Along with labels on containers and SDSs, employee training is one of three core components of a comprehensive hazard communication program. Training is needed to explain and reinforce the information presented on labels and SDSs, to ensure that employees understand the chemical hazards in their workplace and are aware of the protective measures to follow. The new rule includes a relatively minor revision to the HCS training requirements, intended to ensure that labels and SDSs are adequately explained to employees. In light of the evidence previously discussed relating to label and SDS comprehension, the importance of training should not be underestimated.

Training is necessary to ensure that employees understand the standardized heading and sequence of information on SDSs. Employees must be able to understand the meaning of the standardized label elements in order for them to be effective. In certain instances, label elements already appear to be fairly well understood. For example, "Danger" already appears to be generally recognized to represent a higher degree of hazard than "Warning". Other label elements, particularly some pictograms, are less well understood. This is not surprising given the limited amount of exposure that most of the population has had to these pictograms. It is reasonable to assume that all other requirements for training employees and maintaining a hazard communication program will remain the same as they are under the current standard.

It is a longstanding OSHA position that employees have the „right to know" and understand the hazards of chemicals they are exposed to in the workplace. This knowledge is needed in order to take the precautions necessary for safe handling and use, to recognize adverse health effects associated with chemical exposure, and to respond appropriately in emergency situations.

The purpose of the HCS is to provide information so that workers and employers can take the appropriate steps to protect themselves. When workers are trained to recognize and prevent hazards they can be instrumental in recognizing unsafe conditions, taking preventative action, and alerting management. The HCS requires employers to inform workers about the general requirements of the standard, operations where hazardous chemicals are present, and the location of the written HCS program, MSDSs, and hazardous chemical inventory.

In addition, employers are required to specifically train workers in the methods used to detect the presence or release of a hazardous chemical, the physical and health hazards of the chemical, and control measures (including work practices, emergency procedures, and personal protective equipment).

PART TWO:

HOW IS THE HAZARD COMMUNICATION/GHS STANDARD ENFORCED?

Chapter 4 – Part II

How will the Hazard Communication/GHS standard be Enforced?

Chapter Highlights:

- **How to Avoid Hazard Communication Fines?**
- **How will the OSHA Inspector examine our Written Hazard Communication Program?**
- **How will the OSHA Inspector examine our Labels?**
- **How will the OSHA Inspector examine our Training program?**
- **How will the OSHA Inspector examine our Safety Data Sheets?**

There are approximately 2,000 federal and state OSHA inspectors responsible for enforcing safety regulations at more than seven million workplaces. They are responsible for the health and safety of 130 million workers, which translates to about one compliance officer for every 60,000 workers. They conduct unannounced inspections of places where employees work.

If they discover conditions or practices that they think are in violation of OSHA requirements citations and penalties against the employer will soon follow.

The federal government enforces OSHA in 23 of the 50 states, the District of Columbia and the Virgin Islands. State government employees run the program in the other 27 and in two US Territories (Puerto Rico and the Virgin Islands). Those 27 states and territories are known as State Plan states.

OSHA has delegated its enforcement authority to the state government in the so-called State Plan states.

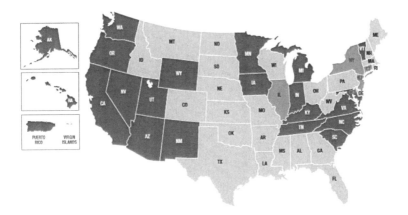

Figure 4.1 State Plan State: The light gray shaded states below are Federal OSHA. The states that are dark gray are called State Plan States.

The federal government inspectors are part of OSHA, the US Labor Department's Occupational Safety and Health Administration. The state inspectors have the same power as OSHA inspectors and, for the most part, they enforce the same requirements. Some states plans meet or exceed federal standards and may in fact have additional rules and regulations that are not part of federal standards.

How are Inspection Targets Chosen?

The particular places that OSHA CSHO's (Compliance Safety and Health Officers) inspect are chosen according to an OSHA inspection plan (or program). There are several different ones. OSHA enforces regulations by inspecting workplaces, issuing citations, and imposing monetary penalties for violations of OSHA safety and health standards. Inspections are conducted by compliance officers, usually without advance notice. In states that have their own plans, inspections are conducted by state inspectors. Workplace inspections must be conducted at a reasonable time, generally during the employer's normal work hours, and in a reasonable manner. When an OSHA compliance officer arrives for a workplace inspection, you have the right to deny entry and to demand that OSHA obtain a warrant to inspect your premises. OSHA may get a warrant from a judge in a simple and speedy fashion in advance of a proposed inspection or after being denied entry. Your failure to object to the inspection or ask for a warrant constitutes voluntary consent.

Representatives of the employers and employees are entitled to accompany the OSHA inspector on the "walk around" tour of the workplace. The compliance officer may interview employees privately during the course of the inspection.

When an employer grants the inspector entry for a limited inspection, such as one responding to an employee complaint, it may object to expansion of the inspection to other areas of the workplace. If an employer allows the inspector to enter but objects to the inspection of certain portions of the workplace or interferes with or limits any important aspect of the inspection, such as the taking of photographs or videotapes, attaching sampling devices, or questioning employees, OSHA will consider this a refusal of entry.

How to Avoid OSHA Hazard Communication Fines

OSHA recently announced heavy fines against a company for **1).** Failure to develop and implement a Written Hazard Communication program and **2).** Failure to maintain Material Safety Data sheets.

There were fines for other failures; yet the two mentioned above are especially notable as they rank third on OSHA's top 10 list of most frequently cited standards meaning it's no secret OSHA is targeting HCS compliance when it visits worksites more importantly, they are among the easiest of OSHA's standards to comply with.

The Hazard Communication Standard can be broken into 4 Parts:

1. **Written Plan;**
2. **Labels;**
3. **Safety Data Sheets; and**
4. **Training.**

1) Written Plan – You need to have a written plan for your HCS program. This plan should be reflective of your workplace and the hazards that your employees face in their day-to-day working environment. The written plan needs to include a current list of all hazardous chemicals. It also must identify who is responsible for the written plan and outline how all written materials can be accessed. Next, the plan needs to describe how your facility meets the requirements for labeling, SDS management and training. Keep in mind, the written plan is the first thing an OSHA inspector will ask for. **See the Appendix for an Example of a Written Hazard Communication Plan.**

2) Labels – The next component of the HCS regulation is making sure that all of the chemicals listed in your plan are labeled properly and appropriate hazard warnings are posted in your work areas. Make sure that products shipped into your facility have labels that are legible and prominently displayed. Also, make sure that you have a good secondary label program to ensure the chemicals are properly identified. In the United States, labels and warnings are only required to be printed in English. If your workforce is multi-cultural, however, you may want to consider printing in secondary languages or making use of common pictograms and symbols to more effectively communicate the hazards.

3) Safety Data Sheets or (MSDSs) – An SDS or MDS as we used to know it. This will tell you everything you need to know from the hazards associated with a chemical, how to handle and store the chemical, to the proper personal protective equipment to use when handling the chemical. According to the HCS, you must have an SDS for all the chemicals in your inventory. You must make the SDSs readily accessible to your employees. And your employees must be trained on where to find and how to read SDSs so they fully understand the risks associated with the chemicals and the protection they need to use when handling chemicals in the workplace.

4) Training – Training is critical to make sure people understand the hazards in their workplace and how to do their jobs safely. The HCS requires that you train your employees on where to find your written plan and SDSs. And, more importantly on how to read the SDSs, labels on containers and warning signs. One final note on training, which may seem obvious, but is often overlooked, make sure employees are trained before assigning them to work with hazardous chemicals.

Written Hazard Communication Program Explained

"...a guy from OSHA's here and wants to see our safety manuals."

The HCS applies to any chemical which is known to be present in the workplace in a manner that employees may be exposed, regardless of whether the employer has created the chemical exposure. The mere presence of a hazardous chemical in the workplace does not trigger coverage under the standard. There must be actual or potential exposure to an employee. Compliance Safety Health Officers (CSHOs) shall review the employer's written hazard communication program to determine if all applicable requirements have been addressed. The HCS obligates all employers, including those on multi-employer worksites, who may expose their employees to hazardous chemicals to develop a written program.

All employers with employees who may be, exposed to hazardous chemicals must develop, and maintain at each workplace a written hazard communication program. Programs must be developed whether the employer generates the hazard or the hazard is generated by other employers. Multi-employer worksites are those establishments where employees of more than one employer are performing work. The MSDS/SDS information exchange or access requirements pertain to employers who introduce hazardous chemicals into the worksite and expose another employer's employees.

It requires an employer on a multi-employer worksite to include the methods he/she will use in his/her program to provide other employers with on-site access to SDSs. This covers each hazardous chemical to which the other employers' employees may be exposed. Therefore, one employer does not have to physically give the other employer the SDSs but rather must inform others of the location where the SDSs will be maintained. (For example, in the general contractor's trailer). The HCS allows employers to decide on the method of information exchange.

It also requires employers to make the written program available upon request to employees, OSHA and NIOSH, in accordance with the requirements of 29 CFR 1910.1020(e). This requirement means that the employer must provide a copy of the written program within the time periods discussed in 1910.1020 (for example, no later than 15 working days after the request for access is made).

How will the OSHA Inspector examine our Written Hazard Communication Program?

The written program should be reviewed first by management and prior to ascertaining whether the elements of the program have been implemented in the workplace. The written program is your document that spells out how your company will be in compliance and should have the following:

Labels	Yes	No	Completed Date
1. Is there a designated person(s) responsible for ensuring labeling of in-plant containers?			
2. Is there a designated person(s) responsible for ensuring labeling on shipped containers?			
3. Is there a labeling system(s) used?			
4. Are there Pictograms on all labels and employees understand them?			

Safety Data Sheets			
1. Is there a designated person(s) responsible for obtaining/maintaining the SDSs?	**Yes**	**No**	**Completed Date**
2. How are the data sheets to be maintained (in notebooks in the work area(s), in a pick-up truck at the jobsite, via fax), are there procedures on how to retrieve SDSs electronically, including back-up systems to be used in the event of failure of the electronic equipment, and how employees obtain access to the SDSs?			
3. Are there procedures to follow when the SDS is not received at the time of the first shipment?			
4. Is there a procedure for updating the SDS when new and significant health information is available?			

Employee Information &Training	Yes	No	Completed Date
1. Is there a designated person(s) responsible for conducting training?			
2. Is there a format of the training program to be used (audiovisuals, classroom instruction?			
3 .Are the procedures to train new employees at the time of their initial assignment and to train employees when a new hazard is introduced into the workplace?			
4. Are the procedures to train employees regarding new hazards to which they may be exposed to when working on or near another employer's worksite (i.e., hazards introduced by other employers)?			
5. Is a there a list of the hazardous chemicals as part of the written program?			

6. Are employees informed of the hazards associated with chemicals contained in unlabeled pipes in their work areas?	Yes	No	Completed Date
7. Are there methods regarding how employees will be trained on potential hazards at other worksites they may visit and at multi-employer worksites?			
8. For multi-employer workplaces, are the methods the employer will use to inform the other employer(s) of the labeling system used clearly described?			
9. Does the written plan include the methods the employer will use on multi-employer worksites to provide other employers with on-site access to SDSs?			
10. Is the written program made available to employees and their designated representatives upon request?			

Labels and Other Forms of Warning Explained

Labels or other markings on each container must include the identity and appropriate hazard warnings, including target organ effects of the hazardous chemical. Labels on shipped containers must also include the name and address of the chemical manufacturer, importer, or other responsible party among other information.

Labels provide an immediate warning of the hazards to which employees may be exposed and also provide a link to other sources of more detailed information. Labels must contain the identity of the chemical, the name and address of the responsible party, and appropriate hazard warnings.

The standard's definition of hazard warning has been amended to specifically include target organ effects:

> "Any words, pictures, symbols, or combination thereof appearing on a label or other appropriate form of warning which convey the specific physical or health hazard(s), including target organ effects, of the chemical(s) in the container(s)."

The HCS clearly states that employees exposed to health hazards must be apprised of both changes in body functions and the signs and symptoms that may occur to signal those changes.

The definitions for "physical" and "health" hazard explain which hazards must be covered. The hazard warning must convey the particular hazards of the chemical, including target organ effects. Statements such as **"Caution,"** **"Danger,"** are precautionary statements and are not to be considered appropriate hazard warnings. If, inhaled, chemical cause's lung damage, then the appropriate hazard warning is **"lung damage,"** not inhalation.

The label is intended to be an immediate visual reminder of the hazards of a chemical. It is not necessary, however, that every hazard presented by a chemical be listed on the label. The safety data sheet is used for this purpose. Manufacturers, importers, and distributors will have to assess the evidence regarding the product's hazards and must consider exposures under normal conditions of use or in foreseeable emergencies when evaluating what hazards shall be put on the label. This is not to say that only acute hazards are to be listed on the label, or that well-substantiated hazards should be left off the label because they appear on the safety data sheet.

An employer's obligation to label in-plant containers and of hazardous chemicals requires that appropriate hazard warnings appear on the label. Alternatively, an employer may provide general information regarding the hazards of chemicals, as long as other information required by the HCS is immediately available to employees.

Employers using alternative labeling systems must ensure that their employees are aware of all information required to be conveyed under the HCS. OSHA will make a plant-specific determination of the effectiveness of the complete program when an inspection is conducted. Any employer who relies on one of these types of alternative labeling systems, instead of using labels containing complete health effects information will in any enforcement action alleging the inadequacy of the labeling system bear the burden of establishing that it has achieved a level of employee awareness which equals or exceeds that which would have been achieved if the employer had used labels containing complete health effects information.

The key to evaluating the effectiveness of any alternative labeling method is to determine whether employees can correlate the visual warning on the in-plant container with the applicable chemical and its appropriate hazard warnings. The alternative labeling system must also be readily accessible to all employees in their work area throughout each work shift.

How will the OSHA Inspector examine our Labels?

Compliance Safety and Health Officers (CSHOs) shall determine that the container is labeled and that the labels are legible, and that the labels are prominently displayed. Labels must be in English. Labels and SDS's may also be printed in additional languages.

1. The CSHO shall determine whether the label identity can be cross-referenced with the SDS and the list of hazardous chemicals?
2. The CSHO must consider alternate labeling provisions (for example tags or markings) for containers which are of unusual shape or proportion and do not easily accommodate a legible label?
3. The CSHO shall evaluate the effectiveness of in-plant labeling systems through a review of the employer's training program and SDS procedures. Such evaluation shall include interviews with employees to determine their familiarity with the hazards associated with chemicals in their workplace. An effective labeling system is one that ensures that employees are aware of the hazardous effects (including target organ effects) of the chemicals to which they are potentially exposed too?
4. Chemical manufacturers, importers, and distributors shall be cited for deficiencies relating to products that are shipped downstream. Violators of the standard shall be cited when a hazardous chemical is created or used in-house only?
5. No citations will be issued on when an indefinite stay-of-enforcement has been placed on the requirement that manufacturers update label information within 90 days of becoming aware of significant information regarding the hazards of the chemical.

Safety Data Sheets Explained

Safety Data Sheets are an essential component of the GHS and are intended to provide comprehensive information about a chemical in the workplace. Information provided on SDSs must be accurate. The safety and health precautions must be consistent with the hazards of the chemical. It serves as a source of information about chemical hazards and to how to obtain advice on safety precautions. The SDS is normally product related and not specific to workplace; nevertheless, the information on an SDS enables the employer to:

> **Develop an active Safety & Health Program of worker protection measures including training which is specific to the workplace.**

The Hazcom standard now requires a Safety Data Sheet (SDS) to have all the 16 sections of information on it. Although, a company can have a SDS that does not have all the 16 sections of required information on it. Section 12 – 15 of the SDS sheet is not required. It is only optional.

SDSs must be in English. This requirement was included to prevent importers of chemicals from supplying SDSs in a foreign language. This requirement, however, does not prevent a chemical manufacturer from translating SDSs from English into foreign languages, in order to assist non-English speaking employees with training comprehension and hazard recognition.

SDSs must include a telephone number for emergency information. There is no requirement that the responsible party staff a telephone line with personnel who can respond to an emergency 24 hours-a-day. The hours of emergency line operation are determined by the chemical manufacturer and should be set after considering the thoroughness of the SDS, the health/physical hazards of the chemical, the frequency of use and immediacy of information needs, and the availability of information through alternative sources

> The SDS must be updated only when its preparer becomes newly aware of significant hazard information or ways to protect against the hazards of a chemical. The standard requires that these changes be added within three months of becoming aware of the information.

Chemical manufacturers and importers have an affirmative duty to provide SDSs to distributors and employers upon initial shipment and also upon request. Thus, a chemical manufacturer and/or importer shall be cited under if they withhold sending SDSs to downstream users with an initial shipment, with the first shipment after updating an SDSs, or upon request pending a separate payment for the SDSs.

SDSs must be readily accessible and there must be no barriers to employee access during the work shift. OSHA interprets the term **"readily accessible"** to mean immediate access to SDSs. The employer has flexibility to determine how this will be accomplished. The use of electronic means such as computers with printers, microfiche machines, the Internet, CD-ROMS, fax machines, is acceptable.

Employers using electronic means to supply SDSs to their employees must ensure that reliable devices are readily accessible in the workplace at all times; that workers are trained in the use of these devices, including specific software; that there is an adequate back-up system for rapid access to SDSs in the event of an emergency, including power outages, equipment, and on-line access delays; and that the system is part of the overall hazard communication program of the workplace. Additionally, employees must be able to access hard copies of the SDSs, and in the event of medical emergencies, employers must be able to immediately provide copies of SDSs to medical personnel. Mere transmission of the requested information orally via telephone is not acceptable.

Employers may use off-site SDS management services to meet the requirements of the HCS only if SDSs are readily available to employees, either as hard copies in the workplace or through electronic means are ensured. Despite the use of an MSDS management service, the employer maintains primary responsibility for the hazard communication program, including receipt and use of the information to develop and implement a site-specific hazard communication program. When immediate access to paper or hard copy SDSs does not exist, CSHOs will evaluate the performance of the employer's system by requesting a specific SDS Sheet.

Factors that determine if Safety Data Sheets (SDSs) are readily accessible include the following three items:

1. Are the Safety Data (SDS's) Sheets maintained at a location and under conditions where employees can access them during each work shift when they are in their work areas?

2. If an electronic system is used for SDS access (computer, fax, etc.) do employees know how to operate and obtain information from the system? (CSHOs will request an employee to retrieve SDS's using the electronic system.)?

3. Was there an Emergency Accident where immediate access was critical?

Employees must have immediate access to MSDSs and be able to get information when they need it in order for an employer to be in compliance with the Hazard Communication standard.

On multi-employer job sites, employers who produce, use or store hazardous chemicals in such a way that other employers' employees are exposed or potentially exposed, must communicate to other employers how the means of access to MSDSs will be accomplished.

Employees who work at more than one site during the work shift must be able to obtain MSDS information immediately in an emergency. MSDSs may be kept at the primary workplace facility; as long as the employer has a representative available at all times to ensure ready access to this information. This is the only situation in which an employer is allowed to transmit hazard information via voice communication. The employer must address in the written hazard communication program how MSDS information will be conveyed to remote worksites.

There is no small business exception. While employers with 10 or fewer employees don't have to keep injury/illness records and are exempted from some OSHA inspections, they must comply with all OSHA safety and health standards and requirements.

OSHA violations occur when you do not observe all the requirements that apply. Simply running a safe operation is not enough. And ignorance of the law is no excuse. The penalties for non-compliance are severe. Million dollar fines are not unusual.

But that's not all. You could go to jail or be sued for millions even if you have never received an OSHA inspection.

Here is an Example of Not Training an Employee on a MSDS Sheet:

William Boss hired Joe Workman to do some painting. Boss didn't know that Workman had a slight asthmatic condition. Working with the paint severely aggravated Workman's condition. He had to be hospitalized and nearly died. He can never work again. Boss was sued for $10 million because he failed to heed the Material Safety Data Sheet (MSDS) warnings for the paint. They provided that no one should use the paint unless first given a pulmonary function test. The fact that Boss didn't know about the MSDS warnings or Workman's asthma was no defense. There is an OSHA requirement that an MSDS must be obtained for all products that contain hazardous chemicals and that each employer must provide training to his employees on the MSDS provisions. Boss hadn't done that.

How will the OSHA Inspector Examine our Safety Data Sheet's?

Compliance Safety Health Officers (CSHOs) shall evaluate the compliance status of this provision by examining a sample of a Safety Data Sheet (SDSs) to determine that the SDSs have been developed and prepared in with the requirements of the Hazcom standard and to ensure that the information regarding the health and physical hazards is accurate. If SDSs are not updated when new information becomes available, the initial hazard determination performed by the chemical manufacturer or importer is deficient. **The following questions will be asked by the CSHO in determining the adequacy of your SDSs sheets?**

SDS Sheets	Yes	No	Completed Date
1. Does your employer have a Safety Data Sheet (SDS) for each hazardous chemical used?			
2. Does each SDS contain information which addresses at least the 16 sections by the OSHA standard?			
3. Are all sections of the MSDS completed?			
4. If the CSHO determines that the employer has tried to obtain the SDS and has not been able to do so, a letter and/or telephone call from the supplier or manufacturer will be the appropriate action for this situation. Has this been done?			
5. Employers are not to be held responsible for inaccurate information on the SDS/label which they did not prepare and they have accepted in good faith from the chemical manufacturer, importer, or distributor?			
6. CSHO's will cite a company whenever an inspection reveals an employer does not have an SDS Sheet. Are there completed SDS Sheets on all chemicals?			

	Yes	No	Completed Date
7. On multiple employers' worksites, citations for violations shall be issued to the employer responsible for making the SDS(s) readily accessible. A citation for violation shall be issued if an employer fails to include the methods by which the employer will inform other employers about on-site access to safety data sheets. Are all employees informed?			
8. If an employer on a multi-employer worksite brings hazardous chemicals onto that site and fails to inform other employers about the presence of those chemicals or the availability of the MSDS(s), that employer shall be cited for a violation?			
9. If the employer uses a general contractor or other employer as an intermediary for storage of the SDS(s), and that intermediate employer has agreed to hold and provide ready access to the MSDS(s), then the intermediate employer becomes the controlling employer, and is responsible for ensuring the availability of the SDS(s). The controlling employer (general contractor) therefore, will be cited for a violation of the SDS(s) if the SDS(s) are not available because the subcontractor failed to make them readily accessible, then the subcontractor shall be cited for a violation?			

Employee Information &Training Explained

Employees are to be trained at the time they are assigned to work with a hazardous chemical. The intent of this training provision is to have information prior to exposure to prevent the occurrence of adverse health effects. This purpose cannot be met if training is delayed until a later date.

The training provisions of the HCS are not satisfied solely by giving employees the data sheets to read. An employer's training program is to be a forum for explaining to employees not only the hazards of the chemicals in their work area, but also how to use the information generated in the hazard communication program. This can be accomplished in many ways (audiovisuals, classroom instruction, interactive video), and should include an opportunity for employees to ask questions to ensure that they understand the information presented to them.

Furthermore, the training must be comprehensible. If the employees receive job instructions in a language other than English, then the training and information to be conveyed under the HCS will also need to be conducted in a foreign language.

Additional training is to be done whenever a new physical or health hazard is introduced into the work area, not a new chemical. For example, if a new solvent is brought into the workplace, and it has hazards similar to existing chemicals for which training has already been conducted, then no new training is required. As with initial training, and in keeping with the intent of the standard, the employer must make employees specifically aware which hazard category (for example, corrosive, irritant,) the solvent falls within. The substance-specific data sheet must be available, and the product must be properly labeled. If the newly introduced solvent is a suspect carcinogen, and there has never been a carcinogenic hazard in the workplace before then new training for carcinogenic hazards must be conducted for employees in those work areas where employees will be exposed.

It is not necessary that the employer retrain each new hire if that employee has received prior training by a past employer, an employee union, or any other entity. The employer, however, maintains the responsibility to ensure that their employees are adequately trained and are equipped with the knowledge and information necessary to conduct their jobs safely. It is likely that additional training will be needed since employees must know the specifics of their new employers' programs such as where the MSDSs are located, details of the employer's in-plant labeling system, and the hazards of new chemicals to which they will be exposed.

The Training provision requires that employees be trained on the measures they can take to protect themselves from hazards, including specific procedures the employer has implemented such as work practices, emergency procedures, and personal protective equipment to be used. An employer, therefore, has a responsibility to evaluate an employee's level of knowledge with regard to the hazards in the workplace, their familiarity with the requirements of the standard and the employer's hazard communication program.

Training need not be conducted on each specific chemical found in the workplace, but may be conducted by categories of hazard (for example, carcinogens, sensitizers, acutely toxic agents) that are or may be encountered by an employee during the course of his duties. The training requirements also apply if the employer becomes aware via the multi-employer worksite provision of exposures of his/her employees to hazards for which they have not been previously trained.

Training of temporary employees is a responsibility that is shared between the temporary agency and the host employer. The host-employer holds the primary responsibility for training since the host employer uses or produces chemicals, creates and controls the hazards, and is, therefore, best suited to inform employees of the chemical hazards specific to the workplace environment. The temporary agency, in turn, maintains a continuing relationship with its employees, and would be, at a minimum, expected to inform employees of the requirements of the standard. Contracts between the temporary agency and the host-employer should be examined to determine if they set out the training responsibilities of both parties, in order to ensure that the employers have complied with all requirements of the regulation.

A frequently overlooked portion of the training provisions is that dealing with emergency procedures. The HCS training is expected to be proportional to the hazards of the workplace. If a chemical is very hazardous, more information would be expected to be provided on the SDS. Therefore, the training for emergency procedures, including information about the characteristics of the chemical and precautions to be taken, would need to be more extensive. It requires training of employees on (among other things) the measures employees can take to protect themselves from hazards including emergency procedures and an explanation of the information on the SDSs.

How will the OSHA Inspector Examine our Training Program?

The Hazcom standard requires the training of all employees exposed or potentially exposed to hazardous chemicals. Training programs must be evaluated through program review and discussion with management and employees.

Employee interviews will provide general information to the CSHO regarding the training program. It cannot be expected that employees will recall all information provided in the training and be able to repeat it. Employees must be aware of the hazards to which they are exposed, know how to obtain and use information on labels and SDSs, and know and follow appropriate work practices.

If the CSHO detects a trend in employee responses that indicates training is not being conducted, or is conducted in a fashion that does not meet the intent of the standard, a closer review of the written program and its implementation may be necessary. CSHOs will determine if employees are employed by outside contractors (such as temporary employment agencies) or the inspected employer.

The following questions will be asked used by the CSHO in determining the adequacy of the training program:

Training & Information	Yes	No	Completed Date
1. Has a training and information program been established for employees exposed to hazardous chemicals?			
2. Is training provided at the time of initial assignment and whenever a new hazard is introduced into work areas?			
3. Have all new employees at this location received training?			
4. If electronic access to SDSs is being used at your workplace, have employees been adequately trained to retrieve the information?			
5. If no employee training has been provided OSHA citations will be issued and If there is a deficiency in your training program the employer will be issued citations?			

To Establish if an Employer-Employee Relationship exists, the OSHA Inspector will ask the following Questions:

1. Who controls the manner and means by which work is accomplished?

2. Who supervises/evaluates the work quality?

3. What and where is the location of the work?

4. Who determines the worker's schedule? (Time of arrival/days worked?)

5. Who provides required instruments, tools, and equipment?

6. What is the history and duration of the relationship between the parties?

7. To what extent can the client/host employer choose a particular worker?

8. Who has the right to assign new projects to the worker?

9. What is the extent of the party's control over when and how long the employee works?

Hazard Communication

Compliance Checklist

Date: _____Location: _____

_____

Safety Manager:_____

Phone Number: _____

SAFETY DATA SHEETS (SDS)	Yes	No	Comments/Completion date
A. Is a current SDS is on file for each hazardous chemical?			
B. Is the SDS sheet written in English?			
C. Are all SDSs presented using the following 16 headings in the order given below:			
1. Identification of the chemical or mixture and of the supplier.			

	Yes	No	Comments/Completion date
2. Hazard identification - GHS classification of the substance/mixture and any national or regional information.			
3. Composition information on ingredients - Chemical identity or Common name of the chemical.			
4. First aid measures - Description of necessary measures, subdivided according to the different routes of exposure, i.e. inhalation, skin and eye contact and ingestion.			
5. Fire-fighting measures - Specific hazards arising from the chemical and any special protective equipment and precautions for fire-fighters.			
6. Accidental release measures - Personal precautions, protective equipment and emergency procedures			
7. Handling and storage - Precautions for safe handling and conditions for safe storage.			

	Yes	No	Comments/Completion date
8. Exposure controls/personal protection - Control parameters and occupational exposure limit values or biological limit values and engineering controls.			
9. Physical and chemical properties -Appearance physical state, color, Odor,etc;			
10. Stability and reactivity - Chemical stability; Possibility of hazardous reactions and; Conditions to avoid.			
11. Toxicological information A description of the various toxicological (health) effects and the available data used to identify those effects, including information on the likely routes of exposure (inhalation, ingestion, skin and eye contact.			
12. Ecological information - Mobility in the soil and other adverse effects. **OSHA will not be enforcing information requirements in sections 12 - 15.**			

	Yes	No	Comments/Completion date
13. Disposal information - Description of waste residues and information on the safe handling and methods of disposal, including the disposal of any contaminated packaging.			
14. Transport information - Transport hazard class (es); Packing group and special precautions which a user needs to be aware of, or needs to comply with.			
15. Regulatory information - Safety, health and environmental regulations specific for the product in question.			
16. Other information - Including information on preparation and revision of the SDS.			
LABELS - Information required on a GHS label will include the following:			
1. Signal words - A word used to indicate the relative level of severity of hazard and alert the reader to a potential hazard on the label. Signal words used in GHS are "Danger" and "Warning." Danger is for the more severe hazard categories. Signal words are assigned to each hazard category.			

2. Hazard Statements - A phrase assigned to a hazard class and category that describes the nature of the hazards of a hazardous product, including when appropriate, the degree of the hazard.	Yes	No	Comments/Completion date
3. Precautionary statements Phrase (and/or pictogram) that describes the recommended measures that should be taken to minimize or prevent adverse effects resulting from exposure to a hazardous product. GHS label should include appropriate precautionary information, the choice of which belongs to the labeler or competent authority.			
4. Product Identifier - Label for substance should include the chemical identity of the substance. For mixtures and alloys. Label should include chemical identities of all ingredients or alloying elements that contribute to acute toxicity, skin corrosion or serious eye damage, germ cell mutagenicity, carcinogenicity, reproductive toxicity, skin or respiratory sensitization, or specific target organ toxicity (STOT). When these hazards appear on the label.			

5. Supplier identification - Name, address and telephone number of the manufacturer or supplier of the substance or mixture should be provided on the label.	Yes	No	Comments/Completion date
EMPLOYEE INFORMATION AND TRAINING			
A. Is Training provided to all employees exposed to hazardous chemicals?			
1. Upon initial assignment?			
2. After introduction of a new hazard?			
B. Is a Training log maintained that contains the name of the employee, the instructor and the date of training?			
C. Does the training program cover the following:			
1. The requirements of the Hazard Communication Standard?			

	Yes	No	Comments/Completion date
2. The location of the written Hazard Communication Program and the SDS's sheets?			
3. The methods or observations that may be used to detect the presence or release of a hazardous chemical?			
4. The physical and health hazards of the chemical used?			
5. The measures taken to protect employees from the hazards (work practices, PPE, etc.)?			
6. The employer's labeling system?			
7. How to read and interpret a SDS sheet?			
8. How to obtain and use hazard information?			
9. The methods and observation techniques to determine the presence or release of hazardous chemicals?			

	Yes	No	Comments/Completion date
10. The work practices that may result in exposure?			
11. How to prevent or reduce exposure to hazardous substances?			
12. Personal protective equipment requirements?			
13. The procedures to follow if exposure occurs?			
14. Emergency response procedures for hazardous chemical spills?			
WRITTEN HAZARD COMMUICATION PROGRAM			
A. Is a Written Hazard Communication Program completed?			
B. Is the Written program accessible to all employees?			
C. Does the Written program include the following:			

	Yes	No	Comments/Completion date
1. The name/position of the person responsible for administrating the Hazard Communication Program?			
2. Name of person responsible for all chemical labels?			
3. Type of labeling system used by the employer?			
4. Name of person responsible for obtaining SDSs?			
5. Procedure if the SDS is not received with initial shipment?			
6. Procedure for receiving and updating the master SDS file?			
7. The location of the SDS s?			
8. Provisions for employee access to SDS in the work area?			

	Yes	No	Comments/Completion date
9. The methods used to inform employees of the hazards of non-routine tasks?			
10. The hazards associated with chemicals contained in unlabeled pipes?			
11. The methods used for notifying contractors of the Hazard Communication Program?			
12. A list of the hazardous chemicals used in the workplace (chemical inventory)?			

Chapter 5

GHS N

THE Hazard Communication /GHS

Chapter Highlights:

- Does a company have to provide Safety Data Sheets (SDS's) to a customer?
- The Hazard Communication Standard (HCS) as it pertains to the Electronic Transmittal of Safety Data Sheets (SDSs). Is it acceptable under OSHA Compliance to have the Electronic Transmission, Storage, and Dissemination of SDSs?
- What are "Pictograms"?

General Industry (29 CFR 1910); Construction Industry (29 CFR 1926) Shipyard Employment (29 CFR 1915); Marine Terminals (29 CFR 1917); Longshoring (29 CFR 1918)

Hazard Communication –

Purpose – 1910.1200

What does GHS mean in the Hazard Communication Standard?

GHS stands for the **Globally Harmonized System for the Classification and Labeling of Chemicals. It** is a set of guidelines for ensuring the safe production, transport, handling, use and disposal of hazardous materials The GHS was developed by the United Nations, as a way to bring into agreement the chemical regulations and standards of different countries. In short, it is an international attempt to get everyone on the same page. The GHS is not a global law or regulation it is a system. Think of it as a set of recommendations. No country is obligated to adopt all or even any part of the GHS .Countries can pick and choose those pieces of the GHS they wish to incorporate into their own regulations, and each country remains responsible for its own enforcement.

Does OSHA send you updated Safety Data Sheets (SDSs) for the products your company uses?

No. The Hazard Communication Standard (HCS) requires manufacturers, importers, and distributors to send SDSs with initial shipments to all downstream users, for any item that would expose employees to hazardous chemicals. OSHA does not provide SDSs to employers. We suggest that you contact the manufacturer or distributor of the products to request updated SDSs. If the manufacturer or distributor will not send you an SDS, you may contact your OSHA area office for enforcement action.

What Hazardous Chemicals need to be communicated to employees upon their hire? Can I give them a copy of all of our hazardous Chemicals (by name) in a single document, or do I only give them the name of chemicals they may be handling in their specific department? Furthermore, what is a "hazardous chemical"?

Before they start work, employees must be informed of the chemicals in their work area. Along with a list of chemicals in their work area, employees must be informed of the location of the written hazard communication program and MSDSs/SDS, any operations where chemical are present and training on how to read labels and MSDSs/SDS. They must also receive training on how to detect a release of a hazardous chemical and how to protect themselves. It's up to the chemical manufacturer to provide an MSDS/SDS on a chemical that determine its hazards. Here are some guidelines to help you prepare your list of hazardous chemicals.

Identify Hazardous Chemicals in the Workplace.

The standard requires a list of hazardous chemicals in the workplace as part of the written hazard communication program. The list will eventually serve as an inventory of everything for which an MSDS/SDS must be maintained. At this point, however, preparing the list will help you complete the rest of the program since it will give you some idea of the scope of the program required for compliance in your facility.

The best way to prepare a comprehensive list is to survey the workplace. Purchasing records may also help, and certainly employers should establish procedures to ensure that in the future purchasing procedures result in MSDSs/SDS being received before a material is used in the workplace.

The broadest possible perspective should be taken when doing the survey. Sometimes people think of "chemicals" as being only liquids in containers. The HCS covers chemicals in all physical forms - liquids, solids, gases, vapors, fumes, and mists whether they are "contained" or not. The hazardous nature of the chemical and the potential for exposure are the factors which determine whether a chemical is covered. If it's not hazardous, it's not covered. If there is no potential for exposure (for example, the chemical is inextricably bound and cannot be released), the rule does not cover the chemical.

Look around. Identify chemicals in containers, including pipes, but also think about chemicals generated in the work operations. For example, welding fumes, dusts, and exhaust fumes are all sources of chemical exposures. Read labels provided by suppliers for hazard information. Make a list of all chemicals in the workplace that are potentially hazardous. For your own information and planning, you may also want to note on the list the location(s) of the products within the workplace, and an indication of the hazards as found on the label. This will help you as you prepare the rest of your program.

After compiling the complete list of chemicals, you should review them to determine if any of the items can be eliminated from the list because they are exempted materials. For example, food, drugs, and cosmetics brought into the workplace for employee consumption are exempt. So rubbing alcohol in the first aid kit would not be covered.

Once you have compiled as complete a list as possible of the potentially hazardous chemicals in the workplace, the next step is to determine if you have received material safety data sheets or safety data sheets for all of them. Check your files against the inventory you have just compiled. If any are missing, contact your supplier and request one. It is a good idea to document these requests, either by copy of a letter or a note regarding telephone conversations. If you have MSDSs/SDS for chemicals that are not on your list, figure out why. Maybe you don't use the chemical anymore. Or maybe you missed it in your survey. Some suppliers do provide MSDSs/SDS for products that are not hazardous. These do not have to be maintained by you. You should not allow employees to use any chemicals for which you have not received an MSDS/SDS. The MSDS/SDS sheet provides information you need to ensure proper protective measures are implemented prior to exposure in the workplace.

Does a company have to provide Safety Data Sheets (SDS's) to a customer?

No. Food or alcoholic beverages which are sold, used or prepared in a retail establishment (e.g., a grocery store, restaurant or drinking places) are exempt from the provisions of the HCS. Food items such as peanut butter therefore are not covered under the HCS. Furthermore, SDSs are not required by the HCS if the "chemical" is not hazardous as defined by the standard. It is the manufacturer's responsibility to make this determination. Quite often, however, SDSs are transmitted by the manufacturer for reasons other than compliance. In this situation, OSHA has encouraged manufacturers to provide a statement on the SDS clarifying that the product is not considered a hazardous chemical under the HCS. In the absence of such a statement, we would suggest that you contact the product manufacturer for further explanation.

What is the Purpose of the Hazard Communication Standard?

It is to ensure that the hazards of all chemicals produced or imported are evaluated and that information concerning their hazards is transmitted to employers and employees. This transmittal of information is to be accomplished by means of comprehensive hazard communication programs, which are to include container labeling and other forms of warning, safety data sheets, and employee training. All employers are required to provide to their employees information about any hazardous chemicals known to be present in the workplace to which employees may be exposed under normal conditions of use or in a foreseeable emergency. As an employer you are required to develop and maintain at each workplace, a written hazard communication program, labels and other forms of warning, safety data sheets, and employee information and training will be met for your employees who may encounter hazardous materials during the course of their employment.

Scope & Application -

1910.1200 (b)

When will the revised Hazard Communication/GHS standard go into effect?

The new Hazard communication/GHS regulation establishes the following two dates. **1).** It requires employers to train employees regarding the new labels and safety data sheets by 2 years after the publication of the final rule, and **2).** It mandates that chemical manufacturers, importers, distributors, and Employers come into compliance with all provisions by 3 years after the publication of the final rule. During the transition period, employers would be required to be in compliance with either the existing HCS or the modified GHS, or both. OSHA recognizes that hazard communication programs will go through a period of time where labels and safety data sheets under both standards will be present in the workplace. This will be considered acceptable, and employers are not required to maintain two sets of labels or safety data sheets for compliance purposes.

What are the New changes to the Hazard Communication /GHS standard that our company needs to know?

The most noticeable changes brought by the GHS for all companies will be the changes to safety labels and safety data sheets. As an example, the GHS refers to safety data sheets as SDSs, dropping the M from the material safety data sheets (or MSDSs) most American companies are used to. The GHS also standardizes the content and formatting of SDSs and:

1. Defining health, physical and environmental hazards of chemicals
2. Creating classification processes that use available data on chemicals for comparison with the defined hazard criteria
3. Communicating hazard information as well as protective measures on labels and safety data sheets.
4. Hazard classification
5. Labels
6. Safety Data Sheets and
7. Training.

Are there Other Regulatory Agencies involved in this Final Rule besides OSHA that we should be concerned with?

Yes. In the United States, GHS/Hazcom adoption is under four government agencies:

1. Occupational Safety & Health Administration (OSHA). www.osha.gov/hazcom/global.html
2. Environmental Protection Agency (EPA). http://www.epa.gov/oppfead1/international/globalharmaon.htm
3. Department of Transportation (DOT). http://hazmat.dot.gov/regs/intl/globharm.htm
4. Consumer Product Safety Commission (CPSC). http://www.cpsc.gov/phth/GHSpolicy.html

OSHA served as the lead U.S. agency on the classification of chemicals and hazard communication and changes to its Hazard Communication Standard. It is expected to affect over 40 million workers in 5 million workplaces. To date, only the DOT has implemented significant components of the GHS into its standards.

Is the HAZCOM Standard applicable to an Office Environment?

No. Office workers who encounter hazardous chemicals only in isolated instances are not covered by the rule. OSHA considers most office products (such as pens, pencils, adhesive tape) to be exempt under the provisions of the rule, either as articles or as consumer products. OSHA has previously stated that intermittent or occasional use of a copying machine does not result in coverage under the rule. However, if an employee handles the chemicals to service the machine, or operates it for long periods of time, then the program would have to be applied.

Is a Safety Data Sheet (SDS) required for Non-Hazardous Chemicals?

No. SDSs that represent non-hazardous chemicals are not covered by the HCS. The standard requires that "the employer shall maintain in the workplace copies of the required SDSs for each hazardous chemical, and shall ensure that they are readily accessible during each work shift to employees when they are in their work area(s)." OSHA does not require nor encourage employers to maintain SDSs for non-hazardous chemicals. Consequently, an employer is free to discard SDSs for non-hazardous chemicals.

Are pharmaceutical drugs in a retail establishment which is packaged for sale to consumers exempt from the Hazard Communication standard (HCS)?

Yes, the HCS exempts, "food, drugs, cosmetics, or alcoholic beverages in a retail establishment which are packaged for sale to consumers," and "foods, drugs, or cosmetics intended for personal consumption by employees while in the workplace.

If the Manufacturer cannot provide a SDS for a covered drug, must the Pharmacy document attempt to obtain a SDS?

Yes, the pharmacy is to contact the drug manufacturer, importer, or distributor to request a SDS. This action should be documented in the form of a letter. The Hazard Communication standard states that "the employer shall have a SDS for each hazardous chemical they use." However, employers are not to be held responsible for inaccurate information on the SDS which they did not prepare and they have accepted in good faith from the chemical manufacturer, importer, or distributor.

What are the requirements to obtain Safety Data Sheets from manufacturers of drugs and other products which are not received by a hospital in final form?

Manufacturers and distributors of hazardous chemicals (including drugs that are not otherwise exempted from the rule) are required to provide a Safety Data Sheet (SDS) with the first shipment to downstream employers (including hospitals), and with the first shipment after the SDS is updated. Employers must have SDSs for each hazardous chemical in the workplace to which employees are exposed. If one is not received with the shipment, the employer must obtain one.

The Hazard Communication standard requires the SDS to be provided to the downstream user(s) by the chemical manufacturer or importer. Your system requires the SDS to be sought out by the downstream user(s).

I work at a Small Business where we use chemical products such as thinners, adhesives, and paints. Could you please clarify whether or not the use of consumer art products by employees would meet the consumer products exemption under the Hazard Communication Standard?

The consumer product exemption of the HCS applies to the use of those products only if the employer can demonstrate they are used in the same manner (e.g., with the same frequency and duration of use) as a normal consumer would utilize them. In the scenario you provided, the employees are performing operations related to their normal work requirements. During the execution of these duties they may be utilizing art chemicals such as paints, thinners, and adhesives. If the employees are routinely exposed to these hazardous chemicals, then they would be required to be afforded the chemical hazard information available through SDS and hazard communication training. It is the responsibility of the employer to determine employee exposure and ascertain if the frequency of use/exposure is indeed not more than that which would be experienced by a normal consumer.

 **My Office purchases products such as Windex and Office Cleaner so that their employees may clean their work stations. Would the office cleaning products used by my employees come under the consumer products exemption of the HCS and not require a Safety Data Sheet or Training?**

 **No.** You have indicated that these products are provided by your employees to use for the occasional cleaning of work stations and not in situations related to a required work assignment. If your employees utilize the office cleaning products you mention (**Windex and Office Cleaner**) with the frequency and duration as that of a normal consumer, then the use of those cleaning chemicals would fall under the HCS exemption for consumer products and not require a Safety Data Sheet or Training.

The Hazard Communication Standard (HCS) as it pertains to the electronic transmittal of Safety Data Sheets (SDSs). Is it acceptable under OSHA compliance to have the electronic transmission, storage, and dissemination of SDSs?

Yes, the HCS is a performance-oriented standard, and OSHA has avoided mandating any one particular format for achieving compliance with this standard. However, OSHA has issued general guidance for manufacturers (including importers and distributors) and employers when utilizing electronic technologies for transmission of and access to SDSs. This guidance follows:

Manufacturers (Importers, Distributors)

- The manufacturer must ensure that the downstream user has agreed to this type of information access.
- The manufacturer cannot require the downstream user to purchase new technology in order to obtain hazard information.
- The manufacturer must ensure that some positive and verifiable form of notification (such as a letter or e-mail) is provided with all of the information necessary to access the MSDS(s).
- The manufacturer must ensure that some positive and verifiable form of notification is provided to ensure that the downstream user is aware when MSDSs are updated due to significant changes in health hazard

information or ways to protect against the chemical.

Employers

- The employer must ensure that SDSs are readily accessible and that there are no barriers to employee access. This includes ensuring that reliable devices are readily accessible in the workplace at all times.
- The employer must ensure that workers are trained in the use of these devices, including specific software.
- The employer must ensure that there is an adequate back-up system for rapid access to hazard information in the event of an emergency including power-outages, equipment failure, on-line access delays, etc.
- The employer must ensure that the system of electronic access is part of the overall hazard communication program of the workplace.
- The employer must ensure that employees are able to obtain hard copies of the MSDSs, if needed or desired.
- In case of emergency, the employer must ensure that mechanisms must be immediately available to provide emergency response personnel with hard copies of SDSs.

It has been a long-standing policy of OSHA that the transmission of Hazard information over the phone is not acceptable. It is also important to note that liability of service companies which assist manufacturers or employers in converting SDS information into an electronic format. These service companies are considered third-parties to the standard and are not recognized entities under the HCS. Therefore, they would not generally be cited for violations of the standard. Despite the use of third-party service providers, manufacturers maintain responsibility for the adequacy and downstream flow of hazard information, and employers maintain responsibility for the adequacy of their workplace programs.

Is there an acceptable alternative to having drivers maintain an in-vehicle library of Safety Data Sheets to cover every commercial sale which may be made during the day?

The HCS is characterized as a performance-oriented standard. This means that your company has the flexibility to comply with the standard in a way that best fits your business practices and meets the performance requirements of the standard.

SDSs are only required to be sent at the time of initial shipment and when the SDS is updated. In terms of alternative compliance strategies, you may want to consider utilizing electronic SDS copies on computer laptops with printers or fax-modems as a solution to transporting the hard copies of SDS. The ultimate solution is yours as long as there are no barriers to the flow of information to the downstream users of the hazardous chemicals.

Hazard Communication

Definitions -1910.1200 (c)

What are the definitions of Pictograms/Precautionary statements and Unclassified Hazards mean?

Pictograms- means a composition that may include a symbol plus other graphic elements, such as a border, background pattern, or color that is intended to convey specific information about the hazards of a chemical. Eight pictograms are designated under this standard for application to a hazard category.

Precautionary statements- mean a phrase that describes recommended measures that should be taken to minimize or prevent adverse effects resulting from exposure to a hazardous chemical or improper storage or handling.

Unclassified hazards- means a chemical for which there is scientific evidence identified during the classification process that it may pose an adverse physical or health effect when present in a workplace under normal conditions of use or in a foreseeable emergency, but the evidence does not currently meet the specified criteria for physical or health hazard classification. This does not include adverse physical and health effects for which there is a hazard class addressed.

Are there changes in the Hazard Communication standard that will affect other OSHA standards?

Yes. OSHA is revising standards in General Industry (29 CFR part 1910),Construction (29 CFR part 1926), and Shipyards, Marine Terminals and Longshoring (29 CFR parts 1915, 1917 and 1918) that contain Hazard communication provisions in order that they will be internally consistent and aligned with the GHS modifications to the HCS. OSHA is proposing to update the language for workplace signs and labels to incorporate the GHS hazard statement and the applicable precautionary statement(s), where required. Most OSHA substance-specific health standards require hazard warning signs, usually for regulated areas, and the language required on the signs varies greatly (*e.g.*, Asbestos, 4-Nitrobiphenyl, 13 Carcinogens, Vinyl Chloride, Inorganic Arsenic, Cadmium, Benzene, Coke Oven Emissions, Cotton Dust, DBCP, Acrylonitrile, Formaldehyde, Methylenedianiline, 1,3-Butadiene, Methylene Chloride, and Lead).

It will also update definitions in Occupational Exposure to Hazardous Chemicals in Laboratories, and the name Material Safety Data Sheets will change to Safety Data Sheets and require information on them to be compliant with GHS in content, and format. OSHA will also be changing its Flammable and Combustible Liquids standard.

What are the State Plan States plans doing after the Hazard Communication Regulation is Final?

The **26 States and territories** with their own OSHA-approved occupational safety and health plans must adopt comparable provisions within six months after the Agency publishes a final standard. These States and territories are: Alaska, Arizona, California, Hawaii, Indiana, Iowa, Kentucky, Maryland, Michigan, Minnesota, Nevada, New Mexico, North Carolina, Oregon, Puerto Rico, South Carolina, Tennessee, Utah, Vermont, Virginia, Virgin Islands, Washington, Wyoming, Connecticut, New Jersey and New York. OSHA also has approved State Plans that apply to State and local government employees only.

Hazard Communication –Hazard Determination – 1910.1200 (d)

Our company produces gaskets and it is considered an "article" under the Hazard Communication Standard (HCS). Articles do not present a hazardous exposure to employees and are exempt from coverage under the standard. Can you tell me whether our product is an "article" or a "hazardous chemical."?

OSHA does not make hazard determinations on a case-by-case basis, since it is the manufacturer who is most familiar with a product's composition, its intended uses, and the potential downstream exposures. We are not generally involved in the hazard determination process until it is brought to our attention that the manufacturer's SDS may be incomplete or inadequate.

A hazardous chemical is any chemical which is a health hazard or a physical hazard. Crystalline silica is considered a Group 1 carcinogen by the International Agency for Research on Cancer (IARC). According to the HCS, any hazardous chemical determined to be a carcinogen by IARC, the National Toxicology Program (NTP), or regulated as a carcinogen by OSHA is considered a carcinogen for the purposes of the HCS and must be designated as such on the SDS. Crystalline silica is clearly a hazardous chemical. An "article" under the HCS is any manufactured item other than a fluid or particle which, **1).** Is formed to a specific shape or design during manufacture, **2).** Has end use function(s) dependent in whole or in part upon its shape or design during end use, and; **3).** Which under normal conditions of use does not release more than very small quantities, for example, minute or trace amounts of a hazardous chemical and does not pose a physical hazard or health risk to employees.

Therefore, if at any time during employee handling of your product (for example, shipping, packaging, installation, or final use), the silica in your product is available for employee exposure (in quantities other than minute or trace amounts), then your product would not be considered an article and the potential health effects must be reported on the SDS.

Hazard Communication – Written Hazard Communication Program – 1910.1200 (e)

Can a Written Program like the Hazard Communication Program be kept solely in an Electronic Format?

Yes. A number of standards require programs that are written and accessible to all employees on site. Examples of these provisions are 29 CFR 1910.1200(e)(4) (Hazard communication), 29 CFR 1910.1030(c)(1)(i) and 1910.1030(c)(1)(iii) (Bloodborne pathogens), and 29 CFR 1910.146(c)(4) (Permit-required confined spaces). Traditionally, these programs have been kept in separate binders in appropriate work areas in order to comply with the standards. Maintaining multiple copies of these manuals can be both challenging and time-consuming.

Placing safety materials, programs, checklists, and forms on a company intranet can provide significant benefits in consistency, ease of use, and accuracy in maintaining and updating these materials in a timely manner. And, just as hard copy programs can be photocopied upon request, so can an electronic version be printed out upon request.

Computers are much more common in the workplace now than when most OSHA standards were written. I agree that in many instances electronic access to programs could be beneficial. Therefore, OSHA would allow a written program to be in either paper or electronic format, as long as the program meets all other requirements of the standard in question.

Where the standard requires that the written program must be made available to employees, the employer must ensure that employees know how to access the document and that there are no barriers to employee access.

What are the interpretations of the Written Hazard Communication Program (HCP) requirements of Employers on Multi-Employer Worksites?

The situation as we understand from your memorandum involves a citation issued to the Department of Defense Contract Management (DCMR) for exposing two of their employees to the same hazards that the employees of the American Fuel Products Company (Am fuel) were exposed to. The DCMR employees were working at the Am fuel worksite. The DCMR did not have a written HCP on-site for its own employees (who were acting as quality assurance representatives) but was relying instead on the written HCP of their "host" employer, Am fuel. According to your description, DCMR's employees "were aware of" and had received hazard communication training from Am fuel, which was provided to them as part of their host employer's hazard communication program. You questioned whether this practice, the use of Am fuel's HCP for the DCMR employees on Am fuel's site, meets the intent of the standard, and if not, what DCMR must do to comply.

All employers with employees exposed to hazardous substances must develop, implement and maintain a written HCP. "Programs must be developed whether the employer generates the hazard or the hazard is generated by other employers." "All employers with employees potentially exposed to hazardous chemicals therefore must have in place an effective written hazard communication program that details how this intent will be met." Each employer must have their own written hazard communication program which must be in place and available to all their employees.

The standard requires that the written HCP specify the methods that employers at multi-employer worksites will use to share information with other employers and employees regarding SDSs and access to them, precautionary measures and any labeling systems used at the workplace. If an employer is going to rely on the information concerning these requirements as set forth in another employer's HCP, he must specifically state so in his own written HCP. In other words, the "guest" or "non-host" employer would have to specify in his written HCP that his method of providing hazard communication information as required is to rely on the methods set forth in his host employer's written program. Employees of the "guest" employer have a right to know and to access the information that must be contained in their employer's hazard communication program. Where they go to get this information is their own employer's written HCP. The methods their employer is going to use to communicate chemical hazard information to them must be set forth in writing in their own employer's written HCP, even if that method involves relying on a host employer's written program.

What are the relationships between the Hazard Communication Standard (HCS), 29 CFR 1910.1200, and Access to Employee Medical Records, 29 CFR 1910.1020, as they relate to maintenance of Safety Data Sheets (SDS) and the Written Hazard Communication Program?

The HCS requires the employer to make available the Written Hazard communication program in accordance with the access to records provisions of 29 CFR 1910.1020. A copy of the Written Hazard communication program is, therefore, required to be made available upon request to employees, or their designated representative within fifteen working days at no cost to the employee or the representative. The HCS neither requires nor prohibits the printing of pocket-size copies of the program for employees.

Apart from the requirements of the HCS regarding the availability of the Written Hazard communication program, the Access to Employee Medical Records Standard has specific requirements for maintaining SDSs as employee exposure records. SDSs, when they indicate a hazard to human health, are specifically defined as employee exposure records in 29 CFR 1910.1020 and are also subject to the access to records provisions of this standard.

Hazard Communication – Labels - 1910.1200 (f)

What are "Pictograms"?

Pictograms means a graphical composition that may include a symbol plus other elements, such as a border, background pattern or color that conveys specific information about a chemical on a label. All hazard pictograms should be in the shape of a square set on a point (diamond). These various pictograms will be on all the labels that are hazardous chemicals. There are a total of 9 Pictograms. **See below:**

1) GHS-Pictogram-Skull and Crossbones - Usage - Acute Toxicity.

2) GHS-Pictogram-Exploding Bomb –Usage Explosives, Unstable Explosives Self-Reactive Substances and Mixtures Organic Peroxides.

3) GHS-Pictogram-Exclamation Mark

4) GHS-Pictogram-Gas Cylinder - Usage- Gases Under Pressure - Compressed Gas- Liquefied Gas -Refrigerated Liquefied Gas - Dissolved Gas.

5) GHS-Pictogram-Corrosion –Usage -Corrosive to Metals -Skin Corrosion / Irritation -Serious Eye Damage / Eye Irritation.

6) GHS-Pictogram-Health Hazard –Usage -Respiratory Sensitization -Germ Cell Mutagenicity -Carcinogenicity -Toxic to Reproduction -Specific Target Organ Toxicity -Specific Target Organ Toxicity - Aspiration Hazard.

7) GHS-pictogram-Flame Over Circle Usage- Oxidizing Gases - Oxidizing Liquids -Oxidizing Solids.

8) GHS-Pictogram-Flame – Usage - Flammable Gases-Flammable Aerosols -Flammable Liquids -Flammable Solids -Self-Reactive Substances -Pyrophoric Liquids -Pyrophoric Solids - Self-Heating Substances and Mixtures -Substances And Mixtures, which in contact with Water, Emit Flammable Gases -Organic Peroxides.

9) GHS-Pictogram-Environment – Usage -Aquatic Toxicity: Acute Aquatic Toxicity.

What does Hazard Statements/Precautionary Statements mean under the Hazard Communication Standard?

Hazard statements -Means a statement assigned to a hazard class and category that describes the nature of the hazards of a hazardous product, including, where appropriate, the degree of hazard, for example:

- Heating may cause an explosion and
- Causes eye irritation

Precautionary statements: - Means to use caution. For example:

- Keep out of reach of children
- Use only outdoors or in well-ventilated area
- Protect from sunlight.

This pictogram refers to less serious the Exclamation Mark. It means skin irritancy/sensitization and applies to many circumstances where the symbol is applied.

 This pictogram reflects serious longer term Health Hazards such as carcinogenicity and respiratory sensitization.

This pictogram means 'Contains Gas under pressure'.

Would a European Union GHS Label be sufficient to meet OSHA's current Hazard Communication Standard?

Yes, as long as the label complies with the provisions of the HCS standard. The HCS was promulgated to ensure that the hazards of all chemicals produced in or imported into the U.S. are evaluated and that information concerning their hazards is transmitted to employers and employees. The transmittal of information is to be accomplished by means of a comprehensive hazard communication program which includes container labeling and other forms of warning covered under 29 CFR 1910.1200(f).

The HCS requires that labels contain the identity of the chemical; appropriate hazard warnings; and the name and addresses for the chemical manufacturer, importer, or other responsible party. The identity of a chemical is the chemical name or common name that is also used on the safety data sheet (SDS), and a hazard warning means words, pictures, symbols, or a combination thereof which conveys the specific physical and health hazards, including the target organ effects .Manufacturers, importers, and distributors must ensure that containers of hazardous chemicals leaving their facilities have labels which contain these elements.

Classification schemes in the EU and other countries may be different from those in OSHA's HCS. These classification schemes may affect the information provided on both the safety data sheet and the label. However, as long as the EU GHS label contains the information required by the HCS, OSHA will consider the EU GHS label sufficient.

What are the Container Labeling Requirements under HAZCOM?

Under HCS, the manufacturer, importer, or distributor is required to label each container of hazardous chemicals. If the hazardous chemicals are transferred into unmarked containers, these containers must be labeled with the required information, unless the container into which the chemical is transferred is intended for the immediate use of the employee who performed the transfer.

Hazard Communication - Safety Data Sheets or (Material Safety Data Sheets) – 1910.1200 (g)

How do I know if my Safety Data Sheets (SDS) are in compliance with the New Hazcom standard?

If your Safety Data Sheets contains the following 16 items then you are in compliance with the Hazard Communication standard. Information in the SDS should be presented using the following headings given below. If they do not contain all of these items then you are not in compliance.

- **Identification**
- **Hazard(s) identification**
- **Composition/information on ingredients**
- **First-aid measures**
- **Fire-fighting measures**
- **Accidental release measures**
- **Handling and Storage**
- **Exposure controls/personal protection**
- **Physical and chemical properties**
- **Stability and reactivity**
- **Toxicological information**
- **Ecological information**
- **Disposal considerations**
- **Transport information**
- **Regulatory information**
- **Other information**

Do I have to keep every Safety Data Sheet that our companies receive?

That really depends on how SDS's are handled at your company. If your employer has a CD-ROM, Internet or fax on demand service for SDS's then maybe not.

If the copies you received are duplicates (and not updated ones) of sheets that you already have in your SDS collection, then there is no requirement to keep the extra copies on hand. However, be sure to carefully check the revision dates on your sheets to make sure there haven't been any changes/updates that you might otherwise overlook! You should you receive an updated sheet automatically.

Does OSHA Really Require Employers to Keep SDSs for 30 Years?

The short answer is No. Based upon careful reading of OSHA Standard 29 CFR 1910.1020, and several letters of interpretation, you are not required to keep safety data sheets, or your old MSDSs, for 30 years.

You are required to keep some record of the identity of the substances or agents to which employees are exposed for 30 years. To that end, OSHA recognizes an SDS as an acceptable record and as you will see, SDS retention may be your easiest recourse.

If you choose not to retain the actual SDS then OSHA requires you to have not only a record of the identity (chemical name if known) of the substance or agent, but also information regarding where and when it was used. *Again, if you do not keep the SDS, then what ever record you do keep must include information about 'where' and 'when' the chemical or substance was used.*

Your responsibilities under Standard 1910.1020 - Access to Employee Exposure and Medical Records should not be confused with your obligations under Standard 1910.1200, which states that you must make SDSs readily accessible to employees during their work shift. Considering that your obligations under 1910.1200 require you to have SDSs, it might make sense just to keep those SDSs for compliance with 1910.1020.

An electronic SDS management tool can help keep you in compliance with both standards.

If I have the same chemical from a different manufacturer, do I need to keep their entire Safety Data Sheet?

Yes. SDS's must be specific to the manufacturer and contain the contact information for the "responsible party". You could get away with one sheet for the chemical if certain conditions are met. You must identity on the label must be able to be cross-referenced to the SDS; All employees must be trained that you are using one SDS as representative of all vendors (so there isn't confusion during an emergency) and, the SDS must be complete and accurate.

Can I throw away old or outdated Safety Data Sheets?

The question is not whether you can, but whether you would dare to do so. A "harmless" chemical may later be found to cause cancer or other disease sometime in the future (asbestos is one good example). It is certainly to your legal benefit to be able to produce documentation showing that you had supplied all the protective equipment and procedures necessary according the SDS you had at the time. In most cases, SDS's may be a part of your OSHA-mandated "employee exposure records" and you would have to retain these for at least 30 years. While this is a remote possibility, it is something to think about from a legal liability standpoint.

I have encountered in providing Safety Data Sheets is that you "use distributors and we do not know when a first shipment to a customer has occurred." OSHA recognizes this difficulty, and has never required manufacturers to automatically provide copies of SDSs to the end use customer. As the manufacturer may have no way of knowing who these customers are. The requirements of the Hazard Communication standard are based upon a downstream flow of information from chemical manufacturers to distributors and/or employers and ultimately, to affected employees are this the way it works?

Your primary obligation in supplying SDSs is to your direct customers, that is, your distributors. You must provide a copy of the SDS with the first shipment to each of your direct customers, and, if the SDS for one of your products is updated, you must send the updated SDS with the next shipment of the product to that direct customer. Your distributors are, in turn, responsible for supplying a copy of the SDS with the first shipment to each of their direct customers, and so on. Therefore, it is not necessary for you to include "a miniature version of the SDS inside every package." However, because this chain of information transmission through the distributor can sometimes be broken, OSHA has added the requirement that manufacturers must provide a copy of the SDS to other "downstream" employers upon request. Your "FAX-on-demand" system can be used to fulfill this requirement.

What if I need a Safety Data Sheet and the manufacturer of the business no longer exists?

OSHA understands that manufacturers who are no longer in business or who have discontinued a product line do not have to provide SDS's. As long as you've made every effort and you don't have any willful violations of any type you are probably looking at a situation where OSHA might note it during an inspection but not assess a penalty.

How come I don't always get Safety Data Sheets when I order chemicals? I thought manufacturers of chemicals were required to give me one for every chemical I purchase?

Yes, they are required. But they are only required to give you one copy:

- **With the first shipment of a particular chemical.**
- **With the first shipment after the SDS has been updated.**
- **Upon request, if you are a distributor or employer.**

The second and third items only occur if you purchase the chemical after the sheet was changed. If you bought the chemical and the sheet was later updated, few firms would even attempt to let you know. But the next time you buy that chemical they have to send you the updated sheet.

For over-the-counter retail or wholesale sales to employers requires the seller to provide the SDS upon request and to post a sign that an SDS is available. If a retailer does not have commercial accounts and does not use the material, then they are only required to provide an employer with the contact information for the distributor, manufacturer or importer who can supply the sheet.

Most manufacturers are happy to provide additional copies of an SDS if you simply contact their customer service department and ask. In fact, many of them have realized the benefit of making all their SDS's freely available on the Internet.

When does a Safety Data Sheet Need to be Revised or Replaced?

You need to replace or revise an SDS when:

- **Any significant change has been made to the chemical compound or;**
- **Research has revealed a health or physical hazard different from what was originally stated; or**
- **If the product has been listed as carcinogenic by a recognized agency.**

According to OSHA a new SDS must be issued within three months if any of these conditions are met. The old SDS should be retained to potentially limit future legal liability.

Do I have to use Hard Copies or can I use a Computer Database to maintain Safety Data Sheets?

Employers can use computer databases because the HazCom standard is performance-based. The employer must meet all of the following requirements, however:

- **SDSs must be readily accessible with no barriers to employee access. This means reliable devices accessible at all times without the employee needing to ask anyone for permission.**
- **Workers must be trained in the use of these devices, including specific software.**
- **There must be an adequate back-up system and written plan for rapid access to hazard information in the event of an emergency including power-outages, equipment failure, on-line access delays, etc.**
- **The system of electronic access is part of the overall hazard communication program; and**
- **Employees must be able to immediately obtain hard copies of the SDSs, if needed.**

The most popular types of electronic format include fax on demand services (that will fax you a copy as soon as you request one), internet-based suppliers, and "in-house" solutions where corporations scan their SDS sheets into a database rather than use a paper filing system. Paperless compliance works only if the employees have "ready access". If your database is accessible to the required employees on your corporate intranet, you'll probably be

OK. This assumes that you have a written contingency plan to access SDS information in the event of a power failure or other emergency.

What does the term "ready access" requirement and what is a "barrier" to ready access mean?

The Hazard Communication Standard says the following:

The employer shall maintain in the workplace copies of the required Safety Data Sheets for each hazardous chemical, and shall ensure that they are readily accessible during each work shift to employees when they are in their work area(s).

(Electronic access, microfiche, and other alternatives to maintaining paper copies of the safety data sheets are permitted as long as no barriers to immediate employee access in each workplace are created by such options.)

What are the penalties for NoN-Compliance with Safety Data Sheets requirements?

If you are not compliant with the Safety Data sheet requirement you could face fines up to $70,000 or more depending how they count your violation(s) and whether they were "willful" violations. Most fines for SDS violations are substantially lower. You might simply get a warning if you have only a few minor infractions.

We have a Large Worksite. Does having one site-wide SDS repository to maintain our Safety Data Sheets satisfy OSHA requirements?

It depends. The HazCom standard is a performance-based standard which means that OSHA does not concern itself with how you comply, just that you manage to do it. While your method of managing your SDS collection is flexible, specific criteria you need to meet are:

- **SDS's must be maintained on site (including electronic access methods) and;**
- **SDS's must be readily accessible during each work shift to employees.**

What OSHA requirements are there for Contractors who work on Multi-Employer Worksites?

Each contractor or employer has a responsibility to make sure the hazards of their chemicals (and, therefore, SDS's) are known to all workers on the worksite.

The HazCom standard is **performance-based** meaning that OSHA does not care how the employers share this information as long the employees have no barriers to accessing the information when they need it and the plan for sharing this information in writing. The simplest solution for the multi-employer workplace is to provide each other copies of the SDS's or to add your SDS's to their collection (as long as your employees have access). Of course, other training, labeling etc. may be required; SDS's are only a part of the HazCom standard.

 **Must the pharmacy keep Safety Data Sheets (SDS's) for products that do not contain hazardous chemicals and are intended to be crushed or mixed prior to use?**

SDSs are not required for non-hazardous drugs. SDSs are required to be prepared and transmitted with the initial shipment of all hazardous chemicals including drugs and pharmaceutical products, except for drugs as defined by the Federal Food, Drug and Cosmetic Act which are in solid, final form for direct administration to the patient (i.e., tablets, pills, or capsules) or which are packaged for sale to consumers in a retail establishment.

How does OSHA expect me to organize my Safety Data Sheets or System?

The OSHA HazCom standard is a performance-based standard. That means OSHA is not concerned with *how* you organize your SDS files, only that you "ensure that they are readily accessible during each work shift to employees when they are in their work area(s)". This can be by hardcopy, computer, FAX etc., as long as the employee is able to use your system to find any sheet when he/she needs it. But for those of you who simply file paper copies, how to order your filing cabinet or 3-ring binder is a more difficult question.

Some of my employees don't speak English. Do I have to make any special provisions for these workers?

Yes. The OSHA Hazard Communication Standard 29 CFR 1910.1200 requires that your employees are trained in:

- The hazards of all chemicals they use;
- Labeling and;
- Signs.

SDS's are part of the Hazard communication process and training requirements; if your employees do not understand English and you do not provide training in a language they comprehend then you are not in compliance. "The employer must provide verbal training in a language that is comprehensible". Employers having employees who speak other languages may add the information in their language to the material presented, as long as the information is presented in English as well." The standard says:

> **Each Safety Data Sheet shall be in English (although the employer may maintain copies in other languages as well)."**

Clearly, the language says **"may", not "must"**. But communication can only be effective if the employee understands the SDS and what the labels say. Therefore, it is wisest to err on the side of caution and follow the first interpretation listed above. Remember, all of the same information must be in English as well.

Would OSHA take enforcement action under your current regulations against employers or users of a product that has been appropriately labeled according to European Union GHS requirements?

No. The Employer's obligations under the HCS are distinct from those of manufacturers, importers, or distributors. "Employers are not to be held responsible for inaccurate information on the SDS/label which they did not prepare and they have accepted in good faith from the chemical manufacturer, importer, or distributor. The "responsible party" named on the SDS and the label would be held responsible for the accuracy of the information and potentially subject to citation if a violation of the HCS was determined to exist.

Under what conditions can employers rely on Safety Data Sheets services to make available a specific chemical used by that employer?

OSHA's hazard communication standard requires SDSs for the chemicals used in the workplace to be readily accessible to employees. . OSHA interprets **"readily accessible"** to mean immediate access to SDSs. The employer has flexibility to determine how this will be accomplished and may provide the data sheets via paper copies, computer terminal access, or some other means of providing readable copy on-site." If an employer chooses to use an on-line SDS service, it is the employer's obligation (under the HCS), not that of the access service, to ensure that the SDSs for the specific products being used are available, accurately represent the same hazards as those being used, and that there are no barriers to employee access to the SDSs.

What happens after the retailer's regular business hours or when the manufacturer's facility is closed on the weekend?

It is the manufacturer and not the retailer that is responsible for maintaining an emergency number. The emergency number is used when additional product information is required during a hazardous chemical emergency. Hours of emergency line operation must be decided individually by each chemical manufacturer.

It seems that trying to maintain Safety Data Sheets at the retail level is a waste of time could you please explain this to me?

The requirement to provide safety data sheets (SDSs) to employers who buy their hazardous chemicals from a retail outlet and who request an SDS for the purchased chemical is a requirement of the standard for these types of distributors if they are transmitting hazardous chemicals to downstream employers.

If Safety Data Sheets (SDS(s) are made available via computer terminal and employees are properly trained to access them, is a printer necessary or can the SDS simple be read on the screen?

In terms of employee accessibility, the HCS states that SDSs must be readily accessible to employees when they are in their work areas during their work shifts. The standard also states that **"Electronic access, microfiche, and other alternatives to maintaining paper copies of the safety data sheet are permitted as long as no barriers to immediate employee access in each workplace are created by such options."** This requirement may be accomplished in many different ways; the employer must decide what is appropriate for the particular workplace. The key to compliance with the rule is that employees get the information when they need it. Actual paper copies of data sheets, computer terminal access, FAX, or other means of providing readable copy on-site are permitted, again, as long as no barriers to employee access exist.

Employee Information & Training -1910.1200 (h)

If an Employer has employees who do not  **understand verbal English (re: receive work task instructions in a language other than English), must that employer provide the training information in a language that is Comprehensive?**

Yes. The Hazcom standard requires employers provide employees with information and training on hazardous chemicals in their work area. If the employees are required to receive this information and training do not comprehend verbal English, the employer must inform and train these employees in a language which is comprehensible in order to satisfy the requirements.

Is it OSHA policy to require employers to obtain Safety Data Sheets to ordinary consumer products used by its employees, and to Train the employees in the safe use of these products? While the training is invaluable, there is effort involved in obtaining the needed SDS and conducting the Training?

OSHA does have a policy of not applying the Hazard communication standard to employee use of consumer products when those products are used in the same manner as an ordinary consumer – (for example, when employees would not be exposed to more significant hazards than ordinary consumers due to duration or frequency of exposure). This policy applies to any employer.

> **Any consumer product where the employer can show that it is used in the workplace for the purpose intended by the chemical manufacturer and the use results in a duration and frequency of exposure which is not greater than the range of exposures that could reasonably be experienced by consumers when used for the purpose intended.**

It is possible that small employers, for example, with only five employees, that the range of exposures encountered by the staff would be no greater than that experienced by consumers for products such as dish detergent or floor wax. In that case, no Safety Data Sheet (SDS) would be required. Regarding training, the small employer does not need to train workers on each individual product. Workers must be trained so that they understand the various hazards of the products they work with and how to protect themselves from these hazards. For example, workers need to understand the need for using household rubber gloves with products which can irritate the skin (e.g., many cleaning products), and the need for ensuring adequate ventilation when using products which are inhalation hazards (e.g., floor wax, solvents).

Can a contractor's association Train union employees for training under the Hazard communication standard," or "should each contractor train each employee irrespective of the associations." Is each employer responsible for training under the Hazard Communication Standard?

The HCS is a performance-oriented standard and the goal of the training provisions is to ensure that employees are trained according to those provisions. It is OSHA's position, therefore, that training can be provided by the current employer, a past employer, an employee union, or any other entity. From an enforcement standpoint OSHA field personnel will evaluate an employer's compliance with the training and information provisions of the HCS. If it is determined that an employee has not received training or is not adequately trained the current employer will be held responsible regardless of who trained that particular employee. An employer, therefore, has a responsibility when hiring a new employee, who has been previously trained by someone other than the current employer to evaluate the employee's level of knowledge against the training and information requirements of the standard.

The employer has the responsibility to train employees regarding protective practices implemented in their workplace and to explain the labeling system used and how to obtain and use safety data sheets. Training is crucial to the comprehensive hazard communication program as training explains and reinforces the information presented to employees through the written mediums of labels and safety data sheets. While the HCS provisions are performance-oriented, the minimum information must be presented to assure effective employee training concerning the hazards of the particular job assignment.

As a minimum, training should be given to all your employees prior to job assignments where they will be or potentially could be exposed to hazardous chemicals. Since your employees are contracted to extended job assignments, directly working under the supervision of the other employer, you can possibly work out a contractual agreement for the other employer to provide the training specific to the hazardous materials used at that job site.

For your employees, the training program will most likely be the most important component of your hazard communication program because it can be individualized to your employees' abilities. Every effort must be made to train and effectively warn the employees of exposure to hazardous chemicals at the appropriate level of their understanding in view of their special educational requirements.

Does OSHA expect that every Worker will be Trained and able to recite all of the information on the Safety Data Sheets in the Workplace?

No. Training is to ensure that employees are aware they are exposed to hazardous chemicals, and that they know how to obtain, read, and use the written information on labels and SDSs. As a consequence of learning this information, employees should be following the appropriate protective and emergency measures which have been established by the employer to reduce the risks posed by exposure to the chemical hazards. In the unfortunate event of an injury or illness on the job, it is still the responsibility of the employer to provide appropriate first aid and medical services for the employee.

In the Construction industry, the scope of the Hazcom Standard is to include all Employers with employees exposed to hazardous substances. What is the Training requirement when we receive information on the potential hazards from occupational exposures to the hazardous substances they may be exposed from other Workplaces?

HCS sets performance-oriented employee training requirements in 1926.59(h) in order to ensure that employees are provided with information and training about the hazardous chemicals they work with, both at the time of their initial assignment and whenever a new hazard is introduced into their work area. The standard does require however, that each employer develop and maintain at his workplace a written hazard communication program. The written program must describe how the employer will meet the standard's requirements to provide container labeling, collection and availability of safety data sheets (SDS) and how employee training will be conducted. The written program must also contain a list of the hazardous chemicals in each work area, and the means the employer will use to inform employees of the hazards of non-routine tasks.

If, the workplace has multiple employers on-site, employers are to ensure that information regarding the hazards that are present at the worksite and information on measures employees can take to protect themselves is made available to the other employers on-site. Employers on multi-employer worksites must provide other on-site employers (whose employees may be exposed to hazards not brought onto the worksite by their own employer) with a copy of applicable SDSs, or make them available at a location coordinated by both employers at a convenient on-site location. Allowing a construction contractor to maintain SDSs in his home office (which could be miles away from the actual jobsite) would not afford employees ready access to the hazard information during each work shift, as is their right under the standard. The employer's written hazard communication program and applicable SDSs may be kept anywhere on the jobsite, including a vehicle or contractor's trailer, as long as employees know where to find it.

Is it acceptable to distribute copies of Safety Data Sheets (SDS's) and consider that to be Training?

No. Employers must provide training on hazardous chemicals in an employee's work area when the employee receives his/her initial work assignment and whenever a new physical or health hazard is introduced into the employee's work area. The HCS training requirements are not satisfied by merely providing employees with copies of MSDSs.

"[t]he training provisions of the HCS are not satisfied solely by giving employees the [safety] data sheets to read. An employer's training program is to be a forum for explaining to employees, not only the hazards of the chemicals in their work area, but also how to use the information generated in the hazard communication program. This can be accomplished in many ways (audio visual, classroom instruction, interactive video), and should include an opportunity for employees to ask questions to ensure that they understand the information presented to them."

What is the Requirement for Additional Employee Training whenever New Hazards are Identified?

Whenever the employer receives a new SDS or chemical which compels the employer to evaluate the information provided in the SDS to ascertain whether the new product represents a new health or physical hazard to employees. Training would have to be provided to affected employees when new hazards are introduced into the workplace (not necessarily new chemicals).

The intent of the HCS training is to provide information to employees on the hazards they encounter in the workplace. Retraining can be as simple as a weekly safety meeting that highlights new chemicals in the workplace. As long as the initial training covers categories of chemicals and hazards, and how to read and understand SDSs, retraining would merely have to assure that new products and chemicals are identified to the employees and that the hazards, if any, are recognized.

Who is responsible for Hazard Communication Training of the Temporary Employee?

The Temporary Agency or the Employer?

OSHA considers temporary employment agencies that send their own employees to work at other facilities to be employers whose employees may be exposed to hazards. Since it is your company, which maintains a continuing relationship with its employees, but another employer (the client) who creates and controls the hazards, there is a **shared responsibility** for assuring that your employees are protected from the workplace hazards. The employer has the primary responsibility of such protection. The employer has a responsibility under the Occupational Safety and Health Act.

In meeting the requirements of OSHA's Hazard Communication standard the employer would, for example, be expected to provide the training and information requirements specified by the HCS section (h)(1). Client employers would then be responsible for providing site-specific training and would have the primary responsibility to control potential exposure conditions. The client, of course, may specify what qualifications are required for supplied personnel, including training in specific chemicals or personal protective equipment (PPE). Contracts with your client employer and your employees should clearly describe the responsibilities of both parties in order to ensure that all requirements of the regulation are met.

The Hazard Communication standard requires training on hazardous chemicals in the work area at the time of the initial assignment and whenever a new hazard is introduced into the work place. When does the initial assignment begin and who is responsible for the Initial Training and the on-going Training?

The employer would be expected to provide initial training and employers would be responsible for providing site-specific training, or training to update employees on new hazards in the workplace.

APPENDICES

Sample Written Program

For

Hazard Communication

Plan

(Company Name)

Required elements of a Written Plan -The Written plan are the first thing an OSHA compliance officer (CSHO) will ask to see. Here are the most important elements of the Written program that a OSHA inspector will ask for concerning The Hazard communication Plan:

- Labels and other forms of warning. Including samples of pictograms and what is required on a label.

- Safety data sheets (SDSs; procedures for accessing and maintaining them.)

- Employee Information & Training.

- List of hazardous chemicals.

- Hazards of non-routine tasks.

- Hazards of unlabeled pipes.

- Multiemployer worksites.

- Employee access to the written program.

- **Access to the Written Plan -** The HazCom plan must be readily available to employees, their designated representatives, the Assistant Secretary of Labor for Occupational Safety and Health (or applicable state agency), and the Director of the National Institute for Occupational Safety and Health (NIOSH).

- **SDS Access System -** Describe the process for accessing SDSs, including, if applicable, how to access the electronic SDS file system or the services of a fax-back or other offsite SDS retrieval service. The description must include the person(s) responsible for obtaining and maintaining the SDSs, how they are accessed and maintained in the workplace, procedures to follow when the SDS has not been received, and a description of alternatives to obtaining SDS information (the backup system). If the company has a written HazCom plan that adequately describes the SDS access policy and the company can demonstrate that the policy is generally properly implemented, there is much less chance of getting hit with a citation for failing to produce an SDS during a work shift.

- **Multiemployer Worksites -** Any employer that hires the services of an outside contractor or vendor is responsible for ensuring compliance by the contractor with the requirements of HazCom if the contractor's employees may be exposed to chemical hazards while working at the employer's facility. Each contractor bringing chemicals on-site must provide the primary employer with the appropriate hazard information for these substances, including SDSs, labels, and precautionary measures to be taken when working with or around such substances.

- **State Regulatory Requirements** - This plan is based on federal requirements and/or best practices. Some states have laws and regulations that are stricter than federal requirements and may affect how you customize this plan. Check your state for further requirements.

Table of Contents

Information

Page………………………………………………286

Policy Statement…………………………………289

PlanAdministration……………………………...290

    Plan Review and Update…………………………291

    Plan Availability………………………………..292

Definitions………………………………………..293

A Written HazCom Plan…………………………294

Labeling…………………………………………295

Symbols………………………………………...296

Safety Data Sheets (SDSs)……………………302

    SDS Access……………………………………..306

        Primary System…………………………….....306

        Backup System…………………………….....306

    SDS Not Available……………………………..307

    New or Revised SDSs…………………………307

Employee Training and Information……………...308

    Initial Training………………………………….308

    Retraining…………………………………….....308

    Recordkeeping………………………………....308

    Training Content and Format…………………309

Nonroutine Tasks Involving Hazardous Chemicals...310

Informing Other Employers/Contractors…………312

List of Hazardous Chemicals…………………313

Chemicals in Unlabeled Pipes………………..314

Plan Review………………………………………315

Appendices

A. A Sample *Written Hazard Communication Plan*...**366**

B. *Sample letter requesting a Safety Data Sheet*...**399**

C. *Acknowledgement of Receipt of Hazard Communication Training Form*..............**402**

D. *Sample of a Complete SDS Sheet*.........**404**

E. *Sample Contractor Letter*...................**411**

F. *Sample Safety Data Sheet Policy*..........**414**

INFORMATION PAGE

COMPANY NAME:

ADDRESS:

SAFETY COORDINATOR:

LOCATION OF HAZCOM WRITTEN PROGRAM:

LOCATION OF SDSs:

Electronic copies –

Paper copies –

EMERGENCY RESPONSE:

TELEPHONE NUMBERS:

    FIRE:

    MEDICAL:

    SPILL RESPONSE:

DATE PROGRAM IMPLEMENTED:

DATE REVISIONS TO PROGRAM:

Policy Statement

The following hazard communication plan is provided only as a guide to assist employers and employees in complying with the requirements of 29 CFR 1910.1200, as well as to provide other helpful information. It is not intended to supersede the requirements of the standard. An employer should review the standard for particular requirements which are applicable to their individual situation and make adjustments to this program that are specific to their company. An employer will need to add information relevant to their particular facility in order to develop an effective, comprehensive program.

It is the policy of **[company name]** to reduce employee exposure to hazardous chemicals and the overall incidence of chemical-related injuries and illnesses. All employees who are potentially exposed to hazardous chemicals in their assigned jobs must be fully informed of both the hazardous properties of the chemicals and the protective measures that are available to minimize exposure to these chemicals. This type of information will be made available to employees by means of labels on chemical containers, SDSs, and training. Employees will be informed of any known hazards associated with chemicals to which they may be exposed before their initial assignment, whenever the hazards change, or when new hazardous chemicals are introduced into their respective work areas.

Plan Administration

Table [number] provides the roles and contact information for the administration of the hazard communication plan.

■ Table [number]—Program Contact Information

[Modify the table as applicable to your organization.]

Task	Contact Person	Contact Information
Program Administrator	[Name, job title, and department]	Work: [number] Mobile: [number]
Chemical Labeling		Work: Mobile:
Safety Data Sheet (SDS) Inventory		Work: Mobile:
Employee Training		Work: Mobile:

[Name, job title, or department] is responsible for the implementation of the Plan, including reviewing and updating it as necessary.

Labeling - [Name, job title, or department] is responsible for properly labeling all containers of hazardous chemicals and for maintaining and updating the labels.

SDS Inventory - [Name, job title, or department] is responsible for maintaining up-to-date SDSs and ensuring that they are readily accessible in all work areas.

In order to comply with the Hazard Communication Standard, this written program has been established for **(Name of Company)**. All employees of the company are included in this program. Copies of this written program will be available for review by any employee in the following locations:

(Name of Location) _____

_____

Employee Training - [Name, job title, or department]

Is responsible for training employees concerning hazardous chemicals in their work areas.
(Name of Person) _____

Plan Review and Update

This Plan will be periodically reviewed and updated, whenever new hazards are introduced into the workplace.

Plan Availability

Copies of the Hazcom Plan, including the written training program, are available upon request to employees, their designated representatives, the state or federal safety regulatory agency, and to the National Institute of Occupational Safety and Health.

Copies of the Hazcom Plan are available at **[location(s)]**.

_____

_____

_____

_____

_____

_____

Definitions

Chemical — Any chemical compound or mixture of elements and/or compounds.

Hazardous chemical — Any chemical which is a physical hazard or a health hazard.

Safety Data Sheet (SDS) — A written description of a hazardous chemical or chemical product which contains comprehensive technical information about a particular substance and explains the risks, precautions, and remedies to exposure related to hazardous chemicals.

APPENDIX A – Written Hazard Communication   Plan

[Company Name]

Introduction

Regulation: 29 CFR Parts 1910, 1915, and 1926 Hazard Communication Standard.

[Replace with the state regulation if applicable.]

The OSHA Hazard Communication Standard was promulgated to ensure that all chemicals would be evaluated and that information regarding the hazards would be communicated to employers and employees. The goal of the standard is to reduce the number of chemically related occupational illnesses and injuries. This program covers all work operations at **[company/facility   name]** where employees may be exposed to hazardous chemicals under normal working conditions or during an emergency situation.

Labeling

All containers received for use will be clearly labeled as to the contents, note the appropriate hazard warning, and list the manufacturer's name and address.

Label Elements

The GHS provides tables for each hazard class. The tables detail the label elements (symbol, signal word, hazard statement) that have been assigned to each of the hazard categories of the GHS.

Following are the hazard symbols which will be used in the new Hazard Communication/GHS Standard.

Flame	Flame over circle	Exploding bomb
Corrosion	Gas cylinder	Skull and crossbones
Exclamation mark	Environment	Health Hazard

All of the symbols, aside from the environment symbol, are part of the standard symbols used in the new Hazard Communication Standard.

Label Requirements

Information required on a GHS label:

1. Signal Words

A signal word indicates to the reader if a hazard is generally more severe or less severe. The label should include the relevant signal word in accordance with the classification of the hazardous substance or mixture. In case your substance or mixture displays a more severe hazard, the label should bear the signal word *'danger'*, and in case of less severe hazards, it should bear the signal word *'warning'*.

2. Hazard Pictograms

A hazard pictogram is a pictorial presentation of a particular hazard. Accordingly, the classification of your substance or mixture determines the hazard pictograms that should be displayed on your label, for example:

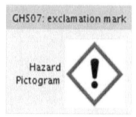
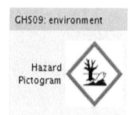

Note: Hazard pictograms should be in the shape of a square set at a point (diamond shape), and should have a black symbol on a white background with a red border.

3. Hazard Statements

Your labels should also bear the relevant hazard statements describing the nature and severity of the hazards of your substance or mixture.

Hazard Class:	For Example:
Physical Hazards	Self-heating in large quantities; may catch fire
Health Hazards	May cause harm to breast-fed children
Environmental Hazards	Very toxic to aquatic life with long lasting effects.

4. Precautionary Statements

Your labels should bear the relevant precautionary statements, giving advice on measures to prevent or minimize adverse effects to human health or the environment arising from the hazards of your substance or mixture. Furthermore, the precautionary statements of one language should be grouped together with the hazard statements on the label.

Precautionary Measurement:	For Example:
General	Keep out of reach of children
Prevention	Keep away from heat/sparks/open flames/ hot surfaces.
Response	Call a poison center or doctor/physician
Storage	Store in a well-ventilated place

5. Supplemental information

Your label should include the relevant supplemental information when the substance or mixture has been classified as hazardous and has the physical or health properties described. The name, address and telephone number of the manufacturer or supplier of the substance or mixture should be provided on the label.

For Example:

Explosive when dry.

Explosive when dry.

Reacts violently with water.

[**Container labeling**] All hazardous chemical containers used at this workplace will clearly identify the chemical on the label, and include an appropriate hazard warning and the manufacturer's name and address. [**Name, job title, or department**] will ensure that all secondary containers in which a substance has been transferred from the original manufacturer's container are labeled with either an extra copy of the original manufacturer's label or with labels marked with the chemical identity, and the appropriate hazard warning.

No container will be released for use until this information is verified. [**Name of person**] will ensure that all containers are labeled.

On individual stationary process containers, we are using [**describe the labeling system such as signs, placards, batch tickets, or process sheets**] rather than a label to convey the required information. Table [**number**] contains the list of stationary process containers and their locations in the facility.

Table [*number*]—Stationary Process Containers

Process Container	Location	Type of Label
[*name*]	[*location name*]	[*name*]

We are using an in-house labeling system that relies on [**indicate the system used, such as NFPA, HMIS, or the in-house system that uses numbers or graphics to convey hazard information**].

[**Name, job title, or department**] will review the organization's labeling procedures every [**frequency**] and will update labels as required.

Safety Data Sheets (SDSs) or Material Safety Data Sheets (MSDS)

[Name, job title, or department] is responsible for maintaining the SDS program. **[Name, job title, or department]** will ensure that procedures are developed to obtain the necessary SDSs, review incoming SDSs for new or significant health and safety information, and will see that any new information is communicated to affected employees.

The new Safety Data Sheet (SDS) is a document that describes the physical and chemical properties of products, substances, and chemicals, their physical/health hazards, and precautions for their safe handling and use in the workplace. The **[Name, job title, or department]** relies on the chemical manufacturers, distributors, and importers to perform hazard determination/evaluation on the chemical products they produce.

The manufacturer, distributor, or importer is responsible to insure the SDS conforms to OSHA requirements, and to provide a Safety Data Sheet for each hazardous chemical product purchased by our company. If there is a revision or change in the SDS information, then the manufacturer, distributor, or importer is required by Federal law to issue an updated SDS to our company.

The Safety Department will maintain a master file of all Safety Data Sheets. The SDSs are stored electronically, in **[location] or** in paper form in the **[location]** area. The paper files are available 24/7/365 to employees covered by the Hazard Communication Program.

In addition to the master file, the Safety Coordinator will provide binders with chemical product inventory lists and corresponding SDSs to each work location where employees are routinely exposed to hazardous substances. The inventory lists and SDSs will be arranged in alphabetical order for ease of identification. All work location binders will be clearly labeled with the Hazard Communication Program. Supervisory personnel in each work location will place the binder in a central area that is easily accessible to all employees during each scheduled work shift. Employees may access this information, without supervisory approval, at any time.

An employee or their representative may request a copy of a Safety Data Sheet (SDS). The employee or representative will be required to complete a request form, which can be obtained in the Safety Department.

Supervisors and individuals that purchase or authorize the purchase of hazardous chemical products for use by employees are responsible to obtain SDSs for those chemicals. If the individual responsible for the purchase of the chemical or product is unable to obtain a Safety Data Sheet, that individual must contact the Safety Manager for assistance. The Safety Manager will contact the manufacturer, distributor, or importer to obtain the SDS.

Documentation on efforts to obtain SDSs will be maintained/retained in the Safety Department.

Chemicals that introduce a new hazard into the work area will be trained on the SDS. Supervisory personnel are responsible to train affected employees on use of and hazards associated with the new chemical product.

Supervisory personnel are responsible to add new/revised/updated copies of the SDSs and chemical/product inventory lists to the work area binders and/or files where the chemicals or products will be used. When a new or revised SDS arrives with shipment of the chemical product, it is the supervisor's or designated staff member's responsibility to forward the original document to the Safety Manager. The Safety Manager will update the central SDS files and hazardous chemical product list whenever a new/revised SDS is received in the Department.

Minimum Information for an SDS

Information in the SDS should be presented using the following 16 headings in the order given below

1. Identification

2. Hazard(s) identification

3. Composition/information on ingredients

4. First-aid measures

5. Fire-fighting measures

6. Accidental release measures

7. Handling and Storage

8. Exposure controls/personal protection

9. Physical and chemical properties

10. Stability and reactivity

11. Toxicological information

12. Ecological information - **Not Mandatory.**

13. Disposal considerations – **Not Mandatory.**

14. Transport information – **Not Mandatory.**

15. Regulatory information – **Not Mandatory.**

16. Other information

SDS Access

SDSs will be readily available to all employees during each work shift. The primary method for accessing SDSs in work areas is **[method, e.g., printed copies, computer system, fax-back service name and phone number]**.

Primary System

Following are the steps that employees will follow to access an SDS:

[Describe the steps employees must follow to access the SDS file system.]

1. **[procedure]**
2.
3.
4.

Backup System

The backup system for accessing SDSs should the primary system fail is **[system description and location]**.

The steps for accessing the SDS backup system are:

1. **[procedure]**
2.
3.

SDS Not Available

If an SDS is not available, or an employee has a problem accessing SDSs, contact **[name, job title, or department]**. If **[name, job title, or department]** is not available, a supervisor will be notified. **[Name, job title, or department]** will ensure that the missing SDS is provided to the employee requesting it by his or her next work shift at the latest, unless the company has not received the SDS from the chemical supplier.

If an SDS is not received at the time of initial shipment, **[name, job title, or department]** will contact the supplier, in writing, to request the SDS. If an SDS is not received from the supplier in **[number; some state rules require no more than 15 days]** days, the company will contact the appropriate government agency for assistance in obtaining the SDS.

New or Revised SDSs

The notice that identifies the person responsible for maintaining SDSs and where the SDSs are located are posted at **[location(s)]**. Employees will be notified at the same location(s) when new or revised SDSs are received. When new or revised SDSs are received, the following procedure will be followed to replace old SDSs:

1. **[procedure]**
2.
3.

Employee Information and Training -
See Appendix B for Acknowledgement of Receipt of Hazard Communication Training.

[Name of person] is responsible for the training Plan and will ensure that all program elements are carried out.

Initial Training

Everyone who works with or is potentially exposed to hazardous chemicals will receive initial training on the Hazard Communication Standard and this Plan before starting work. Before a new hazardous chemical is introduced into any work area of **[company/facility name]**, each employee in the affected work area will be given information and training for the new chemical hazard.

Retraining

Additional training will be conducted by **[name]** when new chemicals are introduced into the work area. Retraining is not required if the new chemical contains hazards similar to previously existing chemicals for which training has already been conducted.

Recordkeeping

All employees attending Hazard Communication training sessions must sign a sheet at the end of the session verifying their attendance. The sheet must contain the date of training and the instructor's name.

Training Content and Format

Each new employee will receive information and training that covers:

- An overview of the OSHA hazard communication standard

- The hazardous chemicals present at his/her work area

- The physical and health risks of the hazardous chemicals

- Symptoms of overexposure

- How to determine the presence or release of hazardous chemicals in the work area

- How to reduce or prevent exposure to hazardous chemicals through use of control procedures, work practices and personal protective equipment

- Steps **[company name]** has taken to reduce or prevent exposure to hazardous chemicals

- Procedures to follow if employees are overexposed to hazardous chemicals

- How to read labels and SDSs to obtain hazard information; and

- The location of the SDS files system and written Hazard Communication Plan.

The training delivery method(s) and format are: **[Describe the training delivery method and format, e.g., hands-on demonstration, audiovisuals, interactive computer programs, and classroom instruction.]**

Non-routine Tasks Involving Hazardous Chemicals

Periodically, employees are required to perform non-routine tasks that may result in temporary exposure to hazardous chemicals. Table **[number]** contains a list of examples of non-routine tasks that are periodically performed by employees, the hazardous chemical(s) involved, and the specific hazard(s) to be avoided.

■ **Table [number]—Non-routine Tasks Involving Hazardous Chemicals**

Non-routine Task	Hazardous Chemical	Hazard(s)
[task description]	[chemical name]	[hazard description]

Employees will not be provided hazardous chemical information and training for such non-routine tasks unless it is determined through a hazard assessment that a hazardous condition exists. Upon request by an employee, **[name]** will provide the employee with information about the hazardous materials he or she may encounter during the non-routine activity.

If it is determined that a hazardous condition exists with the non-routine task, employees performing the task will be provided with information that includes specific chemical hazards, safety measures or protective equipment the employee should use, and steps **[company/facility name]** is taking to reduce the hazards, such as ventilating, providing respirators, and implementing emergency procedures.

Informing Other Employers and Contractors

It is the responsibility of **[name of person]** to provide other employers and contractors with information about hazardous chemicals that their employees may be exposed to on a job site and precautionary protective measures for their employees. It is the responsibility of **[name of person]** to obtain information about hazardous chemicals used by other employers or contractors to which employees of this organization may be exposed.

Other employers and contractors will be provided with SDSs for hazardous chemicals introduced into the work area by **[company/facility name]** in the following manner: **[Describe the multi-employer SDS access policy here, if applicable.]**

In addition to providing a copy of an SDS to other employers, other employers will be informed of necessary precautionary measures to protect employees exposed to operations performed by this organization.

Also, other employers will be informed of the hazard labels used by the organization. Where symbolic or numerical labeling systems are used, the employees of other employers or contractors will be provided with information explaining the labels used for hazardous chemicals to which they may be exposed.

List of Hazardous Chemicals

A list of all known hazardous chemicals used in **[company/facility name]** work areas is attached to this Plan. The list includes the name of the chemical, the manufacturer, the work area in which the chemical is used, dates of use, and quantity used. Further information on each chemical may be obtained from the SDSs.

When new chemicals are received, this list is updated within 30 days. To ensure any new chemical is added to the list in a timely manner, the following procedures must be followed:

1. **[Procedure]**
2.
3.
4.

The hazardous chemical inventory is compiled and maintained by **[name]**.

[NOTE: The chemical list should be arranged so that it can be cross-referenced with the SDS file system and the label system. Additional useful information, such as the manufacturer's telephone number, an emergency number, scientific name, CAS number, the associated task, etc., can be included.]

Chemicals in Unlabeled Pipes

Work activities are sometimes performed by employees in areas where chemicals are transferred through unlabeled pipes. Prior to starting work in these areas, the employees' supervisor should contact **[name of person]** for information regarding:

- The chemical in the pipes
- Potential hazards; and
- Required safety precautions.

Plan Review

This written Hazard Communication Plan for _____(**Name of Company**) will be reviewed by _____(**Name of Employee**) annually and updated as necessary. The Plan was last updated**:**

[Insert date]

APPENDIX B – *Sample Letter Requesting a Safety Data Sheet*

The sample form letter on SDS sheets will be kept on file for all employees who request SDS sheets. You can use this sample as a guide to develop your own form letter.

Employers must maintain a complete and accurate SDS for each hazardous chemical that is used in the facility. They are entitled to obtain this information automatically upon purchase of the material. When new and significant information becomes available concerning a product's hazards or ways to protect against the hazards, chemical manufacturers, importers, or distributors must add it to their SDS within three months and provide it to their customers with the next shipment of the chemical. Employers must have a manufacturer specific SDS for each hazardous chemical used in the workplace.

Sample Form Letter

Date of your request

(Name of manufacturer/distributor you need the SDS from)

(Their address)

(City, state, zip code)

(Their fax number if you make this request)

Subject: Safety Data Sheet Request (SDS)

Please send us the (SDSs) for the following product(s):

(1) ＿＿＿＿

(2) ＿＿＿＿

(3) ＿＿＿＿

Our business requires the SDS(s) listed above to comply with the Hazard Communication Standard. Please make sure that the SDS(s) you send us meet the requirements of the content and distribution of the safety data sheets (SDSs) and label information.

Thank you for your immediate response.

Sincerely,

Your name

Your company's name

Business address

To _____

From _____

I hereby request that I have been given the Safety Data Sheets on the following hazardous substance(s):

_____

_____

_____

_____

_____

_____

_____

_____

Date Received _____

Requesting Employee_____

APPENDIX C –

Acknowledgement of Receipt of Hazard Communication Training

My signature below acknowledges that I have received training concerning The Hazard Communication Standard. I understand that this training fulfills the employee training requirement of OSHA's Hazard Communication Standard.

The jobsite and classroom training included the following:

1. I understand the purpose and scope of the OSHA Hazard Communication Standard.

2. I have reviewed and understand the Written Hazard Communication Program.

3. I understand the definition of classification "hazardous chemical".

4. I understand the new labeling procedures which include the new Pictograms, Hazard statements, Signal words on all the labeling containers.

5. I understand what Safety Data Sheet's (SDS) are. I also understand they must be obtained for each hazardous chemical that our company has.

6. I have received Training on the Hazard Communication Standard.

7. I have been trained and understand all aspects of the new Hazard Communication Standard. Including SDS's, Labels, and Employee information and Training.

_____

EMPLOYEE NAME (**Please print**)

_____

EMPLOYEE SIGNATURE
DATE

_____

EMPLOYEE SIGNATURE
DATE

_____

COMPANY REPRESENTATIVE
DATE

APPENDIX D - *Sample of a Complete Safety Data Sheet (SDS).*

A Safety data sheet (SDS) shall include the information specified below under the section number and heading indicated for sections 1-11 and 16. If no relevant information is found for any given subheading, the SDS shall clearly indicate that no applicable information is available. Sections 12-15 may be included in the SDS, but are not mandatory.

Minimum Information for an SDS Sheet

1.	Identification	(a) Product identifier used on the label; (b) Other means of identification; (c) Recommended use of the chemical and restrictions on use; (d) Name, address, and telephone number of the manufacturer, importer, or other responsible party; (e) Emergency phone number.
2.	Hazard(s) identification	(a) Classification of the chemical in accordance with paragraph (d) of this section; (b) Signal word, hazard statement(s), symbol(s) and precautionary statement(s) in accordance with paragraph (f) of this

		section. (Hazard symbols may be provided as graphical reproductions or the name of the symbol, e.g., flame, skull and crossbones); (c) Unclassified hazards (e.g., combustible dust or dust explosion hazard); (d) Where an ingredient with unknown acute toxicity is used in a mixture at a concentration _ 1%, a statement that × percent of the mixture consists of ingredient(s) of unknown toxicity is required.
3.	**Composition/information on ingredients**	Except as provided for in paragraph (i) of this section on trade secrets: **For Substances** (a) Chemical name; (b) Common name and synonyms; (c) CAS number and other unique identifiers; (d) Impurities and stabilizing additives which are themselves classified and which contribute to the classification of the substance. **For Mixtures**

		The chemical name and concentration or concentration ranges of all ingredients which are classified as health hazards in accordance with paragraph (d) of this section. **For All Chemicals Where a Trade Secret is Claimed** Where a trade secret is claimed in accordance with paragraph (i) of this section, a statement that the specific chemical identity and/or percentage of composition has been withheld as a trade secret is required.
4.	**First-aid measures**	(a) Description of necessary measures, subdivided according to the different routes of exposure, i.e., inhalation, skin and eye contact, and ingestion; (b) Most important symptoms/effects, acute and delayed. (c) Indication of immediate medical attention and special treatment needed, if necessary.
5.	**Fire-fighting measures**	(a) Suitable (and unsuitable) extinguishing media. (b) Specific hazards arising from the

		chemical (e.g., nature of any hazardous combustion products). (c) Special protective equipment and precautions for fire-fighters.
6.	**Accidental release measures**	(a) Personal precautions, protective equipment, and emergency procedures. (b) Methods and materials for containment and cleaning up.
7.	**Handling and storage**	(a) OSHA permissible exposure limit (PEL) and any other exposure limit used or recommended by the chemical manufacturer, importer, or employer preparing the safety data sheet. (b) Appropriate engineering controls. (c) Individual protection measures, such as personal protective equipment.
8.	**Exposure controls/personal protection**	(a) OSHA permissible exposure limit (PEL) and any other exposure limit used or recommended by the chemical manufacturer, importer, or employer preparing the safety data sheet. (b) Appropriate

		engineering controls. (c) Individual protection measures, such as personal protective equipment.
9.	**Physical and chemical properties**	(a) Appearance (physical state, color, etc.); (b) Odor; (c) Odor threshold; (d) pH; (e) Melting point/freezing point; (f) Initial boiling point and boiling range; (g) Flash point; (h) Evaporation rate; (i) Flammability (solid, gas); (j) Upper/lower flammability or explosive limits; (k) Vapor pressure; (l) Vapor density; (m) Relative density; (n) Solubility(ies); (o) Partition coefficient: n-octanol/water; (p) Auto-ignition temperature; (q) Decomposition temperature; (r) Viscosity.
10.	**Stability and reactivity**	(a) Reactivity; (b) Chemical stability; (c) Possibility of hazardous reactions; (d) Conditions to avoid (e.g., static discharge, shock, or vibration); (e) Incompatible

		materials; (f) Hazardous decomposition products.
11.	**Toxicological information**	Description of the various toxicological (health) effects and the available data used to identify those effects, including: (a) information on the likely routes of exposure (inhalation, ingestion, skin and eye contact); (b) Symptoms related to the physical, chemical and toxicological characteristics; (c) Delayed and immediate effects and also chronic effects from short and long term exposure;
12.	**Ecological information (Non-mandatory)**	(a) Ecotoxicity (aquatic and terrestrial, where available); (b) Persistence and degradability; (c) Bioaccumulative potential; (d) Mobility in soil; (e) Other adverse effects (such as hazardous to the ozone layer).

13.	**Disposal considerations (Non-mandatory)**	Description of waste residues and information on their safe handling and methods of disposal, including the disposal of any contaminated packaging.
14.	**Transport information (Non-mandatory)**	(a) UN number; (b) UN proper shipping name; (c) Transport hazard class(es); (d) Packing group, if applicable; (e) Environmental hazards (e.g., Marine pollutant (Yes/No); (f) Transport in bulk (according to Annex II of MARPOL 73/78 and the IBC Code); (g) Special precautions which a user needs to be aware of, or needs to comply with, in connection with transport or conveyance either within or outside their premises.
15.	**Regulatory Information (Non-mandatory)**	Safety, health and environmental regulations specific for the product in question.
16.	**Other Information- Includes date of last preparation.**	The date of preparation of the SDS or the last change to it.

APPENDIX E —*Sample Contractor Notification Letter*

Our Company utilizes various outside contractors to assist in maintaining buildings, grounds, and equipment. When this occurs, this is considered a "multi-employer workplace".

The Safety Manager has developed and implemented a system whereby contractors are informed of the hazardous chemicals in areas where the contractors' employees may be exposed.

To ensure that any outside contractors work safety in any owned or operated facility, the Safety Manager will be responsible to provide the contractor with the following information upon request:

- **A copy of our Hazard Communication Plan;**

- **The location of the SDS files; and,**

- **Information and location for any hazardous substances to which they may be exposed while working on the job site.**

Outside contractors are required to review this information with their employees prior to the start of work at our company. It will be the responsibility of the contractor to notify the Safety Manager overseeing the job site of any hazardous chemicals or substances that may be brought onto the job site. This information will need to be provided to any employee working at the job site.

*Purchasing agents are responsible to convey this information to all outside contractors.

Date

To: **{Name of Person}**

Our Company is required by law The Hazard Communication Program. General Industry (<u>29 CFR 1910</u>); Construction Industry (<u>29 CFR 1926</u>) Shipyard Employment (<u>29 CFR 1915</u>); Marine Terminals (<u>29 CFR 1917</u>); Longshoring (<u>29 CFR 1918</u>) to provide the attached information to all outside contractors that we hire to perform services at our institution.

Please ensure the "**Notice to Contractors**" is attached to, and sent with the original copy of the purchase order.

Please retain a copy of the correspondence in your files.

Thanks for your cooperation and support!

LETTER TO NOTIFY CONTRACTORS

The Occupational Safety and Health Administration (OSHA) require employers to establish a method of communicating information about hazardous chemicals in use at, or introduced to, work areas at our facility. This requirement is specified in the OSHA **Hazard Communication Standard** at General Industry (29 CFR 1910); Construction Industry (29 CFR 1926) Shipyard Employment (29 CFR 1915); Marine Terminals (29 CFR 1917); Longshoring (29 CFR 1918).

This notice is to inform you and your employees that our written **Hazard Communication Program** satisfies this requirement by having available SDS's information on labeling, and protective measures to follow when members of your organization are exposed to hazardous chemicals in our work areas. You may acquire this information by contacting the Safety Manager, **{Name of Person}**, and **{Phone number to contact}.**

Your company/operation may be regulated by the OSHA Hazard Communication Standard. You are advised to obtain a copy of the Standard and to be prepared to satisfy your responsibilities.

Questions regarding the University's program can be directed to the Safety Manager, **{Name of Person}**, and **{Phone number to contact}.**

APPENDIX F – SAMPLE SAFETY DATA SHEET OR (MSDS) POLICY.

Material Safety Data Sheets (MSDS) are developed by chemical manufacturers or importers for each chemical or product supplied to record available scientific evidence used in making hazard determination. They provide the following information for the consumer:

- Chemical and common names(s) of the material(s)
- Physical and chemical characteristics of the material
- Physical and health hazards of the material
- Signs and symptoms of exposure
- Medical conditions aggravated by exposure
- Primary routes(s) of entry
- Permissible exposure limits
- Precautions for safe handling and use
- Applicable control measures
- Emergency and first aid procedures
- Name, address and telephone number of party responsible for preparing the MSDS, and
- Other related material regarding the hazardous material.

Before purchasing a product or material, take into account the possible environmental and health effects and, if possible, consider purchasing a safer or more environmentally friendly product. Contact the safety manager for assistance in reviewing MSDS issues as needed.

Chemical manufacturers and importers must obtain or develop a material safety data sheet for each hazardous chemical they produce or import. Employers must have a material safety data sheet in the workplace for each hazardous chemical they use following the OSHA Hazard Communication standard .

Supervisors of departments shall be responsible for maintaining a current MSDS for each hazardous chemical in their area(s) of responsibility. It must be readily accessible to each employee who may come in contact with the hazardous chemical. Supervisors are also responsible to provide department-specific training on hazardous chemicals for their employees.

The Safety Manager will be responsible for compiling and maintaining the master MSDS files as necessary.

New SDSs/MSDSs

When a new product is purchased, the purchaser must obtain the **SDSs/MSDS** from the product manufacturer or distributor.

Upon receipt of the MSDS, the purchaser will do the following:

1. Make a copy of the MSDS.
2. Put the copy in the appropriate department's MSDS file or binder.
3. Identify the department or trade that will be using the product by placing the name in the upper right corner of the original.
4. Forward the original to the Safety Office:

Updated SDSs/MSDSs

Manufacturers and distributors will occasionally send updated or revised versions of MSDSs already on file. When the purchaser or department using the product receives an updated MSDS, they should follow the steps outlined below:

1. Make a copy of the MSDS.
2. Put the copy in the appropriate department's MSDS file or binder.
3. Identify the department or trade that will be using the product by placing the name in the upper right corner of the original.
4. Forward the original to the Safety Officer:
    a. The updated MSDS will then be filed in the Safety Office.
    b. The old MSDS that has been replaced must also be sent to the Safety Officer for archiving following the below directions.

Occasionally, the Safety department will receive updated MSDS direct from the supplier. If the Safety office knows which department it belongs to, the replacement will be forwarded to that supervisor and they should update their files accordingly.

If you are unable to find an MSDS for your department, you can contact the Safety office for assistance in locating a copy.

Archiving SDSs/MSDSs of materials no longer used or replaced

Material Safety Data Sheets that have been replaced with a newer version and/or MSDSs of discontinued materials must be sent to the Safety Officer to be filed in our MSDS Archives. Use the following form when sending these MSDS to the Safety office.

MATERIAL SAFETY DATA SHEETS TRACKING FORM

Complete this form when you are replacing an SDS/MSDS with an updated sheet or when the material is being discontinued and is no longer present in your department.

SDS /MSDS Product Name: _____

_____

_____

_____

_____

Name and location of Department(s) material was used in:

_____

_____

_____

_____

_____

Check one of the following that applies and fill in appropriate dates: SDS has been updated. Material is still utilized in department.

- **Date Material Use began in Dept.:**
  _____/_____/_____

- **Date MSDS updated:** /_____/_____

- **Material use is discontinued in Department.** /_____/_____

- **Date Material Use began in Dept.:**
  _____/_____

- **Date Material Discontinued in Dept.:**
  _____/_____/_____

Send all replaced or discontinued SDS /MSDS sheets with this completed cover sheet to:

Safety Officer we will maintain this archived SDS /MSDS sheets for 30 years. Contact the Safety Officer with any questions.

GLOSSARY OF TERMS

- A -

Aerosols – Means any non-refillable receptacles made of metal, glass or plastics and containing a gas compressed, liquefied or dissolved under pressure, with or without a liquid, paste or powder, and fitted with a release device allowing the contents to be ejected as solid or liquid particles in suspension in a gas, as a foam, paste or powder or in a liquid state or in a gaseous state. Aerosol includes aerosol dispensers.

Alloy – Means a metallic material, homogeneous the naked eye, consisting of two or more elements so combined that they cannot be readily separated by mechanical means. Alloys are considered to be mixtures for the purpose of classification under the GHS.

American National Standards Institute (ANSI) - Sets voluntary standards for industry. It identifies industrial needs for national consensus standards and coordinates development of such standards.

Aspirations – Means the entry of a liquid or solid chemical product into the trachea and lower respiratory system directly through the oral or nasal cavity, or indirectly from vomiting;

ASTM – Means the "American Society of Testing and Materials".

- B -

BCF – Means "bioconcentration factor".

BOD/COD – Means "biochemical oxygen demand/chemical oxygen demand".

Bureau of Labor Statistics - An agency of the Labor Department that compiles statistics on total injuries and illnesses. These figures are then given to OSHA to use in planning their programmed inspections.

- C -

CA – Means "competent authority".

Carcinogen – Means a chemical substance or a mixture of chemical substances which induce cancer or increase its incidence.

CAS – Means "Chemical Abstract Service".

CBI – Means "confidential business information".

Code of Federal Regulations (CFR) - The official register of the US government that contains all final OSHA regulations. The OSHA standards are part of Title 29, the section of the CFR assigned to labor regulations

Chemical Identity – Means a name that will uniquely identify a chemical. This can be a name that is in accordance with the nomenclature systems of the International Union of Pure and Applied Chemistry

(IUPAC) or the Chemical Abstracts Service (CAS), or a technical name.

Combustible - Any substance with a flash point of more than 100 degrees Celsius.

Competent Authority – Means any national body(ies) or authority(ies) designated or otherwise recognized as such in connection with the Globally Harmonized System of Classification and Labeling of Chemicals (GHS).

Compliance Safety Health Officer (CSHO) - An OSHA inspector. He or she inspects a facility for violations of OSHA standards.

Compressed Gas – Means a gas which when packaged under pressure is entirely gaseous at -50°C; including all gases with a critical temperature £ -50°C.

Contact Sensitizer – Means a substance that will induce an allergic response following skin contact. The definition for "contact sensitizer" is equivalent to "skin sensitizer".

Corrosive To Metal – Means a substance or a mixture which by chemical action will materially damage, or even destroy, metals.

Criteria – Means the technical definition for the physical, health and environmental hazards;

Critical Temperature – Means the temperature above which a pure gas cannot be liquefied, regardless of the degree of compression.

- D -

Dermal Corrosion: – See skin corrosion.

Dermal Irritation: – See skin irritation.

Dissolved Gas – Means a gas which when packaged under pressure is dissolved in a liquid phase solvent.

- E -

EC$_{50}$ – Means the effective concentration of a substance that causes 50% of the maximum response.

EC Number or (ECN$^{\circ}$) – Is a reference number used by the European Communities to identify dangerous substances, in particular those registered under EINECS.

ECOSOC – Means the "Economic and Social Council of the United Nations".

End Point – Means physical, health and environmental hazards;

EU - Means "European Union".

Explosive Article – Means an article containing one or more explosive substances.

Explosive Substance – Means a solid or liquid substance (or mixture of substances) which is in itself capable by chemical reaction of producing gas at such a temperature and pressure and at such a speed as to cause damage to the surroundings. Pyrotechnic substances are included even when they do not emit gases.

Eye Irritation – Means the production of changes in the eye following the application of test substance to the front surface of the eye, which are fully reversible within 21 days of application.

- F-

Fines - Monetary penalty amounts that OSHA will list on a citation. They must be paid by employers who do not contest citations or who mount unsuccessful challenges to have citations overturned.

Flammable Gas – Means a gas having a flammable range with air at 20°C and a standard pressure of101.3kPa.

Flammable Liquid – Means a liquid having a flash point of not more than 93°C.

Flammable Solid – Means a solid which is readily combustible, or may cause or contribute to fire through friction.

Flash Point – Means the lowest temperature (corrected to a standard pressure of 101.3 kPa) at which the application of an ignition source causes the vapors of a liquid to ignite under specified test conditions.

- G -

Gas - Means a substance which (i) at 50 °C has a vapor pressure greater than 300 kPa; or (ii) is completely gaseous at 20 °C at a standard pressure of 101.3 kPa.

General Industry - The OSHA standards in 29 CFR 1910 that apply to most businesses and industry.

GESAMP –Means "the Joint Group of Experts on the Scientific Aspects of Marine Environmental Protection of IMO/FAO/UNESCO/WMO/WHO/IAEA/UN/UNEP."

GHS – Means "the Globally Harmonized System of Classification and Labeling of Chemicals".

- H -

Hazard Communication Standard - The standard most cited by OSHA inspectors. It requires that chemical manufacturers and importers assess the hazards of all chemicals that they produce and furnish detailed information to their customers on those determined to be hazardous. It also requires all employers to provide that information to their employees by means of a written hazard communication program, labels on containers, Material Safety Data Sheets, employee training and access to written records and documents.

Hazard Category – Means the division of criteria within each hazard class, e.g., oral acute toxicity includes five hazard categories and flammable liquids include four hazard categories. These categories compare hazard severity within a hazard class and should not be taken as a comparison of hazard categories more generally.

Hazard Class – Means the nature of the physical, health or environmental hazard, e.g., flammable solid carcinogen, oral acute toxicity.

Hazard Statement –Means a statement assigned to a hazard class and category that describes the nature of the hazards of a hazardous product, including, where appropriate, the degree of hazard.

Hazardous Chemical - Means any chemical that is defined as a hazardous chemical in accordance with the Hazard Communication Standard (29 CFR 1910.1200). Appendices A and B of the Hazard Communication Standard provide criteria for classification of health hazards and physical hazards. Health hazard means a chemical that is classified as posing one of the following hazardous effects: acute toxicity (any route of exposure); skin corrosion or irritation; serious eye damage or eye irritation; respiratory or skin sensitization; germ cell mutagenicity; carcinogenity; reproductive toxicity; specific target organ toxicity (single or repeated exposure); or aspiration hazard. The criteria for determining whether a chemical is classified as a health hazard are detailed in Appendix A of the Hazard Communication Standard (29 CFR 1910.1200).

- I -

IARC – Means the "International Agency for the Research on Cancer".

ILO – Means the "International Labor Organization".

IMO – Means the "International Maritime Organization".

Initial Boiling Point – Means the temperature of a liquid at which its vapor pressure is equal to the standard pressure (101.3kPa), i.e., the first gas bubble appears.

IOMC – means the "Inter-organization Program on the Sound Management of Chemicals".

IPCS – Means the "International Program on Chemical Safety".

ISO – Means International Standards Organization.

IUPAC –Means the "International Union of Pure and Applied Chemistry".

- L -

Label – Means an appropriate group of written, printed or graphic information elements concerning a hazardous product, selected as relevant to the target sector(s), that is affixed to, printed on, or attached to the immediate container of a hazardous product, or to the outside packaging of a hazardous product.

Label Element –Means one type of information that has been harmonized for use in a label, e.g., pictogram, signal word.

LC$_{50}$ (50% lethal concentration) – Means the concentration of a chemical in air or of a chemical in water which causes the death of 50% (one-half) of a group of test animals.

LD$_{50}$ - Means the amount of a chemical, given all at once, which causes the death of 50% (one half) of a group of test animals.

L(E)C$_{50}$ – Means LC$_{50}$ or EC$_{50}$.

Liquefied Gas –Means a gas which when packaged under pressure, is partially liquid at temperatures above-50°C. A distinction is made between.**(i) High pressure liquefied gas**: a gas with a critical temperature between -50°C and+65°C; and **(ii) Low pressure liquefied gas**: a gas with a critical temperature above +65°C.

Liquid - Means a substance or mixture which at 50°C has a vapor pressure of not more than 300kPa (3bar), which is not completely gaseous at 20 °C and at a standard pressure of 101.3kPa, and which has a melting point or initial melting point of 20°C or less at a standard pressure of 101.3 kPa. A viscous substance or mixture for which a specific melting point cannot be determined shall be subjected to the ASTM D 4359-90 test; or to the test for determining fluidity (penetrometer test) prescribed in section 2.3.4 of Annex A of the European Agreement concerning the International Carriage of Dangerous Goods by Road (ADR).

Longshoring - Activities involving the loading, unloading, moving or handling of cargo, ship's stores, and gear, into, in, on or out of any vessel on the navigable waters. These tasks are regulated by OSHA standards in 29 CFR 1918.

- M -

Maritime Industry - Activities that cover wharves, bulkheads, quays, piers, docks, and other berthing locations and adjacent storage or contiguous areas and structures associated with the primary movement of cargo or materials from vessel to shore or shore to vessel, including structures which are devoted to receiving, handling, consolidation and loading or delivery of waterborne shipments and passengers, including areas devoted to the maintenance of the terminal or equipment. These activities are covered under 29 CFR 1917, 1918 & 1919.

Material Safety Data Sheets (MSDS') - Written or printed materials containing information known about chemicals. MSDS' must list the physical and chemical characteristics and hazards; health hazards including signs and symptoms of exposure; any applicable exposure limits; the date of preparation of the MSDS; appropriate emergency and first aid procedures; known control measures, applicable precautions for safe use and handling, including appropriate personal protective equipment; and the name of the chemical manufacturer, importer, distributor or other party responsible for preparing or distributing the MSDS.

MARPOL - Means the "International Convention for the Prevention of Pollution from Ships".

Mixture – Means a mixture or a solution composed of two or more substances in which they do not react.

Mutagen – Means an agent giving rise to an increased occurrence of mutations in populations of cells and /or organisms.

Mutation – Means a permanent change in the amount or structure of the genetic material in a cell;

- N -

NGO – Means "non-governmental organization".

NOEC – Means the "no observed effect concentration".

- O -

Occupational Safety and Health Act (OSH Act) - The OSH Act of 1970 is the statute enacted by Congress that sets forth the law that is carried out by OSHA. The purpose of the Act is "to assure so far as possible every working man and woman in the nation safe and healthful working conditions and to preserve our human resources." The Act strives for maximum effectiveness by covering virtually every person or business organization that employs people.

Occupational Safety and Health Administration (OSHA) - An agency of the US Department of Labor with safety and health regulatory and enforcement authority for most United States' industries and businesses.

OSHA Citation - This is known as the OSHA-2 form. It is entitled "Citation and Notification of Penalty." It includes a description of the alleged OSHA violations and the total applicable penalty amounts.

OSHA Standards - Job safety and health regulations that OSHA expects employers to know about, and to be in compliance with. They can be found in 29 CFR and are designated as follows:

> **1910 - General Industry**
>
> **1926 - Construction**
>
> **1928 - Agriculture**
>
> **1915, 1917, 1918 - Maritime**

OECD – Means "The Organization for Economic Cooperation and Development".

Organic Peroxide –Means a liquid or solid organic substance which contains the bivalent -0-0- structure and may be considered a derivative of hydrogen peroxide, where one or both of the hydrogen atoms have been replaced by organic radicals. The term also includes organic peroxide formulation (mixtures).

Oxidizing gas – Means any gas which may, generally by providing oxygen, cause or contribute to the combustion of other material more than air does.

Oxidizing liquid – Means a liquid which, while in itself not necessarily combustible, may, generally by yielding oxygen, cause, or contribute to, the combustion of other material.

Oxidizing solid – Means a solid which, while in itself not necessarily combustible, may, generally by yielding oxygen, cause, or contribute to, the combustion of other material.

- P -

Penalties - The citations issued by OSHA inspectors usually carry a monetary penalty. All penalties are assessed on the basis of the gravity of the violation, size of the business, good faith of the employer and the employer's history of previous OSHA violations.

Pictogram – Means a graphical composition that may include a symbol plus other graphic elements, such as a border, background pattern or color that is intended to convey specific information.

Precautionary Statement – Means a phrase (and/or pictogram) that describes recommended measures that should be taken to minimize or prevent adverse effects resulting from exposure to a hazardous product, or improper storage or handling of a hazardous product. Product identifier means the name or number used for a hazardous product on a label or in the SDS. It provides a unique means by which the product user can identify the substance or mixture within the particular use setting (e.g. transport, consumer or workplace).

Pyrophoric Liquid – Means a liquid which, even in small quantities, is liable to ignite within five minutes after coming into contact with air.

Pyrophoric Solid – Means a solid which, even in small quantities, is liable to ignite within five minutes after coming into contact with air.

Pyrotechnic Article – Means an article containing one or more pyrotechnic substances;

Pyrotechnic Substance –Means a substance or mixture of substances designed to produce an effect by heat, light, sound, gas or smoke or a combination of these as the result of non-detonative, self-sustaining exothermic (heat-related) chemical reactions.

Physical Hazard - Means a chemical that is classified as posing one of the following hazardous effects: explosive; flammable (gases, aerosols, liquids, or solids); oxidizer (liquid, solid, or gas);self reactive; pyrophoric (liquid or solid); self-heating; organic peroxide; corrosive to metal; gas under pressure; or in contact with water emits flammable gas. The criteria for determining whether a chemical is classified as a physical hazard are in Appendix B of the Hazard Communication Standard (29 CFR1910.1200).

- Q -

QSAR – Means "quantitative structure-activity relationships".

- R -

Readily Combustible – Solid means powdered, granular, or pasty substance or mixture which is dangerous if it can be easily ignited by brief contact with an ignition source, such as a burning match, and if the flame spreads rapidly.

Recommendations on the Transport of Dangerous Goods, Manual of Tests and Criteria – Means the latest revised edition of the United Nations publication bearing this title, and any published amendment thereto.

Recommendations on the Transport of Dangerous Goods, Model Regulations - Means the latest revised edition of the United Nations publication bearing this title, and any published amendment thereto.

Refrigerated Liquefied Gas – Means a gas which when packaged is made partially liquid because of its low temperature.

Respiratory Sensitizer – Means a substance that induces hypersensitivity of the airways following inhalation of the substance.

Reproductive Toxins- Means chemicals that affect the reproductive capabilities including adverse effects on sexual function and fertility in adult males and females, as well as adverse effects on the development of the offspring. Chemicals classified as reproductive toxins in accordance with the Hazard Communication Standard (29 CFR 1910.1200) shall be considered reproductive toxins

RID – Means The Regulations concerning the International Carriage of Dangerous Goods by Rail [Annex 1 to Appendix B (Uniform Rules concerning the Contract for International Carriage of Goods by Rail) (CIM) of COTIF (Convention concerning international carriage by rail)], as amended.

- S –

SAR – Means "Structure Activity Relationship".

SDS – Means "Safety Data Sheet" and in this document is used interchangeably with Material Safety Data Sheet (MSDS).

Self-Accelerating Decomposition Temperature (SADT) – Means the lowest temperature at which self-accelerating decomposition may occur with substance as packaged.

Self-Heating Substance – Means a solid or liquid substance, other than a pyrophoric substance, which, by reaction with air and without energy supply, is liable to self-heat; this substance differs from a pyrophoric substance in that it will ignite only when in large amounts (kilograms) and after long periods of time (hours or days).

Self-Reactive Substance – Means a thermally unstable liquid or solid substance liable to undergo a strongly exothermic decomposition even without participation of oxygen (air). This definition excludes substances or mixtures classified under the GHS as explosive, organic peroxides or as oxidizing.

Serious Eye Damage – Means the production of tissue damage in the eye, or serious physical decay of vision, following application of a test substance to the front surface of the eye, which is not fully reversible within 21 days of application.

Serious Violation - A violation representing substantial probability that death or serious physical harm could result from the cited condition, and that the employer knew or should have known of the condition.

Shipyard - Workplaces, activities and employments, including ship building, repairing, and ship breaking, which are covered under 29 CFR 1915.

Signal Word – Means a word used to indicate the relative level of severity of hazard and alert the reader to a potential hazard on the label. The GHS uses „Danger' and „Warning' as signal words.

Skin Corrosion – Means the production of irreversible damage to the skin following the application of a test substance for up to 4 hours.

Skin Irritation – Means the production of reversible damage to the skin following the application of a test substance for up to 4 hours.

Skin Sensitizer –Means a substance that will induce an allergic response following skin contact. The definition for "skin sensitizer" is equivalent to "contact sensitizer".

Solid - Means a substance or mixture which does not meet the definitions of a liquid or gas.

SPR - Means "Structure Property Relationship".

State Plan States - There are 23 states and two territories that are known as state plan states. A state can operate its own OSHA program if it obtains the Secretary of Labor's approval to do so. Employers in these states are subject only to regulation by their state OSHA agency. Federal OSHA authorities play virtually no enforcement role in these states. These 25 jurisdictions are also eligible for 50 percent federal funding of their OS&H activities. The Department of Labor only requires that every state plan be at least as effective as federal OSHA standards in providing safe and healthful employment.

Substance – Means chemical elements and their compounds in the natural state or obtained by any production process, including any additive necessary to preserve the stability of the product and any impurities deriving from the process used, but excluding any solvent which may be separated without affecting the stability of the substance or changing its composition.

Substance - Which, in contact with water, emits flammable gases means a solid or liquid substance or mixture which, by interaction with water, is liable to become spontaneously flammable or to give off flammable gases in dangerous quantities.

Supplemental Label Element – Means any additional non-harmonized type of information supplied on the container of a hazardous product that is not required or specified under the GHS. In some cases this information may be required by other competent authorities or it may be additional information provided at the discretion of the manufacturer/distributor.

Symbol - Means a graphical element intended to succinctly convey information.

- T -

Threshold Limit Value (TLV) - The air concentration of a material to which nearly all persons can be exposed day after day without adverse effects.

Time-Weighted Average (TWA) - The amount of airborne toxic materials an employee is exposed to, usually over an eight -hour period.

Technical Name – Means a name that is generally used in commerce, regulations and codes to identify a substance or mixture, other than the IUPAC or CAS name, and that is recognized by the scientific community. Examples of technical names include those used for complex mixtures (e.g., petroleum fractions or natural products), pesticides (e.g., ISO or ANSI systems), dyestuffs (Color Index system) and minerals.

Toxic and Hazardous Substances - Any substance which can cause acute or chronic injury to the human body, or which is suspected of being able to cause diseases or injury under certain conditions. Subpart Z of 29 CFR 1910 lists 428 substances that literally cover the alphabet. OSHA considers these to be toxic and hazardous substances, and employers are required to keep the levels of these substances within the permissible exposure limit.

- U -

UNCED – Means the "United Nations Conference on Environment and Development".

UNCETDG/GHS –Means the "United Nations Committee of Experts on the Transport of Dangerous Goods and on the Globally Harmonized System of Classification and Labeling of Chemicals".

Unclassified Hazards- Means a chemical for which there is scientific evidence identified during the classification process that it may pose an adverse physical or health effect when present in a workplace under normal conditions of use or in a foreseeable emergency, but the evidence does not currently meet the specified criteria for physical or health hazard classification. This does not include adverse physical and health effects for which there is a hazard class addressed.

UNITAR – means the "United Nations Institute for Training and Research";

UNSCEGHS – means the "United Nations Sub-Committee of Experts on the Globally Harmonized System of Classification and Labeling of Chemicals".

UNSCETDG - means the "United Nations Sub-Committee of Experts on the Transport of Dangerous Goods".

- V -

Violations - Instances of failure to comply with OSHA standards that will be listed on the OSHA citation.

- W -

Willful Violation - A violation that the employer knowingly commits with plain indifference to the law. In other words, the employer was aware that a hazardous condition existed and that there was an OSHA requirement that prohibited it. However, the employer made no reasonable effort to eliminate it. Penalties of up to $70,000 can be proposed for each willful violation, with a minimum penalty of $5,000 for each violation.

Written Programs - Safety program documentation required by a number of OSHA standards in order for compliance to be achieved. OSHA inspectors often request them. Examples include Hazard Communication and Lockout/Tagout.

Acronyms/Abbreviations -The following abbreviations and acronyms are used in this document.

ANSI: American National Standards Institute
APEC: Asia-Pacific Economic Cooperation
ASTM: American Society of Testing and Materials
CA: Competent Authority
CAS: Chemical Abstract Service
CBI: Confidential Business Information
CFR: Code of Federal Regulations
CG/HCCS: Coordinating Group for the Harmonization of Chemical Classification Systems
CPSC: Consumer Product Safety Commission
DOT: Department of Transportation
EPA: Environmental Protection Agency
EU: European Union
FIFRA: Federal Insecticide, Fungicide and Rodenticide Act
GHS: Globally Harmonized System of Classification and Labeling of Chemicals
HCS: Hazard Communication Standard
IARC: International Agency for the Research on Cancer
ILO: International Labor Organization
IOMC: Inter-organization Program on the Sound Management of Chemicals
ISO: International Standards Organization
LD$_{50}$: Lethal dose 50mg/kg: Milligram per kilogram
MSDS: Material Safety Data Sheet
NAFTA: North American Free Trade Agreement
OSHA: Occupational Safety and Health Administration
OECD: The Organization for Economic Cooperation and Development

QSARs: Quantitative Structure-Activity Relationships

SDS: Safety Data Sheet

SME: Small and medium sized enterprises

TFHCL: Task Force on the Harmonization of Classification and Labeling

TSCA: Toxic Substances Control Act

UN: United Nations

UNCED: United Nations Conference on Environment and Development

UNCETDG: United Nations Committee of Experts on the Transport of Dangerous Goods

UNCETDG/GHS: United Nations Committee of Experts on the Transport of Dangerous Goods and on the Globally Harmonized System of Classification and Labeling of Chemicals

UNITAR: United Nations Institute for Training and Research

WG: Work Group

WHMIS: Workplace Hazardous Materials Information System

WSSD: World Summit on Sustainable Development

INDEX

A

Access to Employee
Exposure and Medical
records, 25,206,210,242,338
Access to the Written Plan,
367,
Accessible to MSDS,
181,241,267,318,327,344,
353,368,
Accidental release measures,
336,389,407,
Acknowledgement of Receipt
of Hazard Communication
Training, 402-403,
Acute toxicity, 43, 44,
47,107,202,288,
Acrylonitrile, 322,
Adhesives, 316,
Aerosols, 44-45, 53,
Agriculture, 7, 36, 40, 46,
Agriculture Chemicals, 38, 41,
Alternative labeling systems,
188,189,275,
Application Comparison, 72-
74
Alaska, 13,323,
Alcoholic beverages, 308,314,
American National Standard
Institute (ANSI), 8,
American National Standard
Institute (ANSI) standard
Z400.1, 252,
Archiving SDSs/MSDSs, 333
Arizona, 13,323,
Article, 323,324,
Asbestos, 322,339,
Assistant Secretary of Labor,
367,
Audiovisuals, 271,286,361
Austrailia, 9

B

1, 3-Butadiene, 322,
Back Up Systems,
270,279,319,343,390,
Batch Manufacturing, 178
Benzene, 233
Bloodborne Pathogens, 325,
Bureau of Labor Statistics, 11,
Building Blocks, 11, 44, 45,
46,

C

13 Carcinogens, 322,
Cadmium, 322,
California, 13,323,
Canada, 8, 41, 43,
Cancer, 339
Carcinogenicity,
45,167,171,201,202,257,287,
288,343,
CD-ROMS, 337,
Checklists, 247,251,271
Chemicals, 4, 6, 7, 18,
25,34,34,40,165,,180,181,188
287,306,307,308,309,339
Chemical Hazards, 12, 14, 15,
19,116,179,191,202,223,277,
288,289,306,313,314,316,320
323,327,334,352,354,357,
358,364,367,374,
Chemical Hazard Information,
18,
Chemical Manufacturers
Association, 252,
Chemical Manufacturers, 5,
14, 16, 38,246,273,276,277,
283,306,310,315,334,351,
355,

Classification, 4, 7, 17, 34,41,43,44,48,52,53,311,

Classifying Chemicals, 4, 20,

Classroom Instruction, 271,286,361,

Code of Federal Regulations (CFR), 12,14,38,40,

Coke Oven Emissions, 322,

Combustible Liquids. *See* Flammable and Combustible Liquids.

Comparison of Old & New Label requirements, 58,

Comparison of the Old & New Hazard Communication Requirements, 58-158

Comparison of the OLD & NEW MSDS Sheets Requirements, 58

Competent Authority (CA) 45, 58,116,177,180,

Inspections, Compliance Officers. *See* Compliance Safety and Health Officers

Compliance Safety and Health Officers (CSHOs) 262,263,264,265,268,276,280 283,289,367,

Composition/information on ingredients, 336,388,405,,

Computers, 279,326,348,

Computer Database, 344

Computer laptops, 320,

Computer system, 305,390,

Computer Terminal, 353

Contingency Plan, 345,

Contractors, 261,312,327,346

Consistency, 5, 12,

Consumer, 4, 34, 38,40,41,44,45,46,48,117, 181,245,347,355,

Consumer Products, 7, 37 40,230,270,316,355,

Consumer Product Safety Commission (CPSC) 8, 10, 24, 40,312,

Container Labeling, 106,171,172,187,374, 188,189,307,309,334,335, 384,

Connecticut, 135,323,

Construction, Industry,16, 25,29,322,359,

Corrosion 194-198,330,

Corrosive to Metals, 51

Cosmetics, 36,307,

CSHOs. *See* Compliance Safety and Health Officers

Cotton Dust, 322,

Crystalline silica, 324,

D

Danger, 172,258,

Dangerous Goods, 47,164,245,

DBCP, 322,

Definitions, 377,

Definitions Comparison, 75-86

Department of Transportation (DOT) 8, 10, 24,165,166,171,312,

Director of the National Institute for Occupational Safety and Health (NIOSH) 367,

Distributors, 14,111,188,274, 276,305,310,314,318,334, 335,350,

Disposal Information, 336,389,409,

District of Columbia, 262,

Downstream User, 315,318,320,352

Drugs, 307,314

Drug Manufacturer, 314,

E

Ecological information, 336,389,409,
Electronic Access (format), 193,194,232,234,239,258, 259,260,268,279,320,325, 326,344,346
Emergency Number, 266,351,
Emergency Planning and Community Right to Know Act (EPCRA) 34
Emergency Responders, 7, 17,18,19,22,117,181,319
Emergency Information & Training, 192,354,
Emergency Procedures, 201, 202,287,288,
Employee Access, 233,240 268,283,319,
Employee Access to Records, 25,205,209
Employee Information & Training, 19, 47,255,271,286, 367,370,392,
Employers, 169,319,
Employer – Employee relationship, 291,
Employee Exposure Records, 339,
Employee Medical Records, 328,
English, 286,348,349,354,
Environment, 199-200,331,
Environmental Hazards, 47,172,311,
Environmental Protection Agency (EPA) 8, 10, 23,41,43,45,312,
Establishments, 50, 78,228
European Union, 8, 41, 43, 334, 335, 350,
European Union Label, 38
Equipment Failure, 319,344,
Exclamation Mark, 187-193,244,247,296,330,

Exploding Bomb, 213-222,329,
Explosives, 43, 51, 52,106,107,135,165,166, 167,
Exposure Controls/Personal Protection, 336,389,407,
Eye Irritation, 107

F

Fax Machines, 279,320,348,
Fax-On-Demand, 337,340,344,
Federal Agencies, 23,
Federal Insecticide, Fungicide, and Rodenticide Act,(FIFRA) 41,
Federal Law, 4,
Federal OSHA, 263,
First Aid Kit, 307,
First Aid Measures 17,336,389,406,
Fire Fighters, 117,207,
Fire-fighting Measures, 336,389,406,
Flame, 201-205,330,
Flame over Circle, 206-212,331,
Flammable, *See also*
Flammable and Combustible Liquids, 46, 56,158,162,236,
Flammable Aerosols, 51, 53,138,
Flammable Gases, 51, 53,137,
Flammable Vapors
Flammable and Combustible Liquids, 51, 56, 57,142,158,162,
Flammable and Combustible Materials, 158,322,
Flammable Liquids. *See* Flammable and Combustible Liquids.

Flammable Solids, 51, 57,107,144,167,
Flash Point, 38, 46,
Food, 307,308,314,
Food additives, 36,221,
Formaldehyde, 322,
Foreign language, 286,

G

Gas, 49,
Gases, 52,
Gas Cylinder, 223-227,330,
Gases under Pressure, 51, 55, 56,140,333,
General Comparison of Old & New Hazard Communication Standard, 59-63
General Industry Standards, 16, 25, 29,322,
Globally Harmonized System of Classification and Labeling of Chemicals. (GHS) 4,5,6,8,10,11,16,17,19,25,26, 27,28,35,38,39,40,41,43,45, 48, 58,165, 191,304,

H

Handling and Storage, 17, 336,389,407,
Harmonizing, 4
Hard Copy, 344,348,
Hazard Categories, 167,111,287,
Hazard Classes, 166,167,171,
Hazard Classification, 5, 7, 11, 17,24,25,49,165,311,
Hazard Communication Definitions, 321,
Hazard Communication Standard (HCS), 6,11,12,14, 15,19,26,2838,43,48,165,173, 180,181200,232,237,242,276, 305,314,315,316,318,322,

328,336,350,359,363,
Hazard Communication Compliance Checklist, 292-301,
Hazard Communication Fines, 265,
Hazard Communication WrittenPlan(Program),5,18,19 171,257,265,268,269,279,280 281,286,306,309,319,325, 326,327,328,334,357,359, 360,361,367,
Hazard Communication Standard (Hazcom), 5, 16, 23, 27,28,34,36,164,173,191,277, 281,287,312,340,348,354, 355,356,361,364,
Hazard Communication Information, 15,171,234,241,327,
Hazard Communication Requirements, 15, 26,
Hazard Communication Training, 316,326,
Hazardous Chemicals. **See Chemical Hazards.**
Hazard Determination/ Classification Comparison, 87-90,127-133
Hazard Identification, 336,389,404,
Hazard Information, 281,319,320,
Hazard Determination, 323,324,
Hazard Pictograms, 43,114,173,176,297,
HazardStatements,6,15,17,20 28,39,41,47,48,175,210,246,2 95,382,
Hazard Symbols, 4, 22, 43,165,
Hazard Warnings, 26, 27, 38,111,177,266,274,334,
Hazardous Chemicals, 12, 14, 35, 37, 38,165,166,170,256, 259,267,271,273,274,276,

281,286,
Hazardous Substances *See also* Hazardous Materials and Toxic Substances.
Hawaii, 13,323,
Health Canada, 45,
Health and Physical hazards,, 4,6,107,150-163,192,,200,257,277,343,
Health Hazards Classes, 108,109,111,171,
Health Hazards Comparison, 134,
Health Hazards, 227-244,256,330,333,
Health care Professionals, 164,169
Hospital, 229
Host-employer, 288,

I

Identity of Hazardous Chemical, 111,177,273,
Identification of the Substance or Mixture and of the Supplier, 336,389,404,
Injuries and Illnesses, 11, 12,281,374,
Indiana, 13,323,
Industrial Hygienists, 19,
In-House labeling, 275,276,287,
Injuries. *See* Injuries and Illnesses.
Independent Contractors, 19
Information Page, 370,
Information & Training Comparison, 111-113
Initial Training, 287,392,
Interactive Video, 200,286,361
International Examples, 39,
International Trade, 7, 15, 19,

Internationally Harmonized, 17,
International Agency for Research on Cancer (IARC 324,
International system, 43,
Internet, 337,
Ionizing Radiation, 207
Iowa, 13,323,
Importers, 5, 38, 16,106,111,246,273,274,276, 278,283,305,310,314,315, 318,334,335,350,
Inorganic Arsenic, 322,
Inspection Plan, 178,
Inspection Targets, 224,
Inspection Warrants, 178,264,
Inspections, See Compliance Safety and Health Officers.
Inspectors. *See* Compliance Safety and Health Officers.

J

Japan, 9

K

Kentucky, 13,323,
Korea, 9,

L

Labels,14,15,16,17,18,22,26, 27,28,36,37,47,106,118,266, 269,276,307,311,367,379
Label Examples, 58,159-162
Label Samples, 100-104
Labels Comparison, 91-97
Labeling of Containers, 5,165,269,
Label Information, 178,
Labeling Requirements, 4, 38, 39,172,177,295,381,
Labeling systems, 7,190,201,

Language, 38
Lead, 322
List of Hazardous Chemicals, 397,
Liquid, 49,
Literate, 18,
Loaned Employees, 19
Longshoring, 2,322,

M

Malaysia, 9
Manufacturing, 4,
Manufacturers, 111,188,274,305,318,324, 334,339,351,
Marine Terminals, 25,322,
Maritime Industry, 16, 30,
Maryland, 13,323,
Material Safety Data Sheets (MSDS), 5, 6.26, 245-251,265,287,307,308,319, 386,
Material Safety Data Sheets (MSDS) Comparison, 102-108
Material Safety Data Sheets (MSDS) management service, 280,
Materials Handling and Storage, 185,
See also Cargo Handling
MDA. See Methylenedianiline
Medical Emergencies, 279,
Medical Records, 25,209,215,
Medical Services and First Aid, 180,181,
Methylene Chloride, 322,
Methylenedianiline (MDA), 322,
Mexico, 9,
Michigan, 13,323,
Microfiche, 279,353,
Minnesota, 13,323,

Mixtures, 35, 42, 43, 49, 170, 178,299,
Multiple Employees, 7, 18,129,130,131
Multi-employer Worksites, 182,186,202,240,268,272, 326,327,346,360,367,369,
Multiple Hospitalization, 11, 15,226
Multiple Hazards/Precedence Comparison, 124-126
Multiple Safety Data Sheets, 7

N

4-Nitrobiphenyl, 322,
National Fire Protection Association (NFPA), 8,301,
National Institute for Occupational Safety and Health (NIOSH), 155, 283,
National Toxicology (NTP) 324,
Nevada, 13,237,
New Jersey, 13,323,
New Mexico, 13,237,
New York, 13,323,
Non-Compliance, 345,
Non–Hazardous Chemicals, 313,
Non–Hazardous Drugs, 347,
Non-Routine Tasks, 359,370,394-395,
North Carolina, 13,323,

O

Occupational Exposure to Hazardous Chemicals in Laboratories, 26,322,
Occupational Safety and Health Act, 363,
Occupational Safety and Health Administration (OSHA), 10, 24, 39,165166,312,
Occupational Safety and Health Administration (OSHA) Enforcement, 255,
Office Cleaner, 317,
Office Environment,313,
Office Workers7, 313
On-Line Access, 319,344,
Oregon, 13,323,
Organic Peroxides, 51,154
OSH Act. *See* Occupational Safety and Health Act.
OSHA Compliance, 11, 21, 225, 242,
OSHA Inspections, 8,9,35,132, 220,237,244,195,281,283, 289,
OSHA Requirements, 7, 8, 21,220,253,256,262,292
OSHA Standards, 19, 25, 27,265,326,
Other Information, 336,389,410,
Outside Contractors, 289, 327,328,368,
Oxidizing Gases, 51, 55,107,140,167,
Oxidizing Liquids, 51,152,
Oxidizing Solids, 51,153,

P

Paints, 230,
Performance Oriented (**based**), 16, 28, 39,165,232,318,320,343,347, 348,356,357,359,
Permit-required confined spaces, 325,
Pesticides, 4, 36, 41, 45, 46, 48,116,164,245,
Pharmacy, 347,,
Pharmaceuticals, 36,314,
Physical and Chemical Properties, 336,389,408,
Physical Hazards Comparison, 134
Physical & Health Hazards, 4, 6, 41, 42, 43, 47, 49,168-169,171,173,273,287,334, 248,276,298,311,361,362,
Physical & Environmental Hazard Symbols, 21,
Pictograms, 5,6,15,17,20,22, 28, 47, 48,166,321,329,381,
Plan Administration, 374,
Plan Availability, 376,
Plan Review, 370,
Plan Review and Update, 375,
Power Outages (**failures),** 279,258,345,
Precautionary measures, 37,
Precautionary Statements, 15, 27, 28,113,175,187,210,321, 383,
Precautiontionary Labeling Standard, 36
Preparation and revision of the SDS Sheet, 168,209
Primary System, 306,390,
Printer, 279,
Printed Copies, 305,390,
Product Identity, 41,
Product Identifier, 22,113,175,210,

Puerto Rico, 13,323,
Purpose Comparison, 49,
Pyrophoric Liquids, 51,148
Pyrophoric Solids, 51,148
Pyrotechnic substances, 52

R

3-Ring Binder, 348
Readily Access,
193,233,345,350,360,
Recordkeeping, 392,
Regulatory Agencies, 7,
Regulatory information,
336,389,410,
Retail Establishment,
314,347,351,
Retraining, 277,392,
Revised Safety Data Sheet
(SDS), 391,
Right to know, 173
Risk Management systems,
34,

S

Safety and Health Programs,
12,165,
Safety Data Sheet (SDS
Access, 284,305,390,
Safety Data Sheet Sheets
(SDS), 4,11,14,15,16,17,18,
19, 20, 26,36,41,47,252,
267,274,276,277,283,284,
285,288,305,307,308,309,310
311,317,318,319,322,327,
334,337,339,340,341,345,
346,347,348,349,350,351,
352,353,355,356,358,359,
360,361,362,367,370,386,
387,388,
Safety Data Sheet (SDS)
Management Services, 280,

Safety Data Sheet (SDS) Not
Available, 391,
Safety Meeting, 277,
Safety Professionals, 19
Safety Requirements, 8,
Sample Contractor
Notification Letter, 411-413,
Sample of a Complete Safety
Data Sheet, 404-410,
Sample Letter Requesting a
Safety Data Sheet, 399-401,
Sample Safety Data Sheet
Policy, 414-418
Sample Written Hazcom Plan,
366-418,
Scope Comparison, 64-71
Secondary Label Container,
114,266,275,
Self Heating Substances, 149
Self Reactive Substances,
51,145
Sensitizers, 288,
Shipyard Employment,
25,322,
Signal Words, 6, 15,17,20,28,
40,41,47,48,113,118,174,209,
295,381,
Skin Corrosion, 44,167,
Skin Irritation, 167,
Skull and Crossbones, 183-
186,329,
Small Business, 281,316,
Solid, 49,
South Carolina, 13,323,
Specialized Terminals. *See*
Marine Terminals, Facilities
and Equipment.
Stability and reactivity,
336,389,408,
Standard Industrial
Classification Codes (SIC),
15, 16,17,62,78,228,229,230
Standards. *See* OSHA
Standards.
Standardizing, 4, 5, 15,
18,255,257,

State Plan States and Territories, 13,262,263,323

State Regulatory Requirements, 369,,

Substance- Specific Data Sheets, 287,

Substances corrosive to Metal, 158

Substances in Contact with Water Emit Flammable Gases, 51,150,

Substance Specific Health Standards, 25, 26,322,

Supplemental Information, 300,384,

Supplier Identification, 39,114,176, 211,

Symbols, 47,172,173,174,266,295,334,

Trade Secrets, 250,275,279,

Trade Secrets/CBI Comparison, 114-124

Transportation, 47,

Transport, 7, 14,36,45,46,118,182,304,

Transport information, 336,389,410,

Transportation Pictograms, 20, 41,

Train employees, 5,258,310,343,358,

Training, 19, 26,258,267,286,287,288,290, 311,317,319,354,355,358, 361,362,364

Training Content & Format, 393,

Training Program, 190,200, 203,204,230,276,286,289,

TrainingRequirements, 349, 359

T

Target Audiences, 38, 44,45,46,49,116,164,255,

Target Organ, 111,187,273,334,

Tennessee, 13,323,

Temporary Agency, 202,203,288,363,

Temporary Employees, 202, 363,

Terminal Facilities and Equipment. *See* Marine Terminals.

Texas, 12

Thinners, 316,,

ToxiFlam, 38, 39, 40, 41,42

Toxic Substances Control Act. (TSCA).23,

Toxic and Hazardous Substances, 205,206,207

Toxicological information, 336,389,409,

Trade, 7,208,

U

Unclassified Hazards, 321,

Unlabeled Pipes, 272,370,397,

Unmarked Containers, 249,

United Nations, 304,

United Nations Model Regulations on the Transport of Dangerous Goods, 20, 22, 49,

United Nations Subcommittee for GHS, 4

United States (U.S.) 10,

United States (U.S.) Senate Subcommittee on Employment, Safety, and Training, 254,

Updating Labels, 179,

Updating Labels Comparison, 100-101

Updating MSDS/SDS Comparison, 109-110

Updating SDS's, 246,
US Territories, 12,262,
Utah, 13,323,

V

Vermont, 13,323,
Virginia, 13,323
Vinyl Chloride, 322,
Virgin Islands, 13,323,

W

Warning Signs, 258,322,
Warrants. *See* Inspection
Warrants.
Washington, 13,323,
Windex, 317,
Workplace Hazardous
Materials Information System
(WHMIS) 39,
Workplace Labeling
Comparison, 97-99,177,
Workplace, 4,40-41,116,180,
Written Compliance Program
or Plan, 266,325,
Written Programs,
26,272,289,326,
Work Environment, 100,107,
Workplace, 44,45,46,47,
Workplace Chemicals, 40,
Wyoming, 13,323,

X

Xylene, 254-255